TALES *of* XAVIER

ALES of XAVIER

By JAMES E. WALSH

Maryknoll Missioner
Titular Bishop of Sato

SHEED & WARD   •   *New York*

B-Jes
F w

Editor's Note

⊄ The stories in this book are based on incidents recorded in the life of Saint Francis Xavier. ⊄ The stories have been elaborated according to the formula employed by historical novelists. The bare outlines of the original episodes have been filled in with imaginative detail in order to render them lifelike. The incidents are related in chronological order. ⊄ Some of the stories have already appeared in "The Field Afar," the Maryknoll magazine, but for the most part they now see the light of day for the first time.

CONTENTS

KNIGHT of the THORN

FOR five whole minutes he pursued his investigations with absorbed interest. He had to do a fine piece of wriggling to get started in the first place. He slid off the low divan backwards when nobody was looking. His legs buckled. Landing on his stomach and finding himself intact, he decided he had been rather clever. He promptly set out on his self-conducted tour.

He circumnavigated the Bishop's chair while that good man was in animated conversation with his father. Twice he stopped to examine designs on the rug under the apparent impression that they were something to eat. His efforts to pick them off the carpet resulted in grasping the empty air, so he passed on looking for more worlds to conquer. He crawled around another pair of feet and behind the long table. Coming out on the other side, he found himself back where he had started from. The arched legs of the big chair yawned invitingly. It took some balancing and maneuvering to insert himself into the snug little hideaway, but he managed it.

It was then that he began to feel tired. His ardor for exploration suddenly deserted him. Surveying the new situation, he found it rather cramping. How had he got himself into such an impenetrable forest? He was surrounded on all sides by legs, some belonging to the chair and some belonging to the Bishop. This was not to be borne. He

1

raised his head incautiously to look for a way out and bumped it soundly on the underside of the chair. He let out a wail.

The next thing he knew, he was riding up the broad stairway on a satin-covered shoulder. He looked down to see the faces in the big room grow dim and vanish, and for a moment he had half a mind to kick his legs and make a protest. He did not want to leave the company. But only for a moment. The next second he forgot about it. The shoulder was soft and familiar and he was tired. He snuggled down on it and felt drowsy. He was almost asleep.

"Bless me, Sweet Mother." He heard the words but he did not know what they meant. He opened his eyes and saw his mother bending over him. He vaguely thought she was speaking about somebody like herself yet a distinct somebody else. His fat, little hand was taken and pushed to his forehead, then to his breast, then to each shoulder. "In the Name of the Father and of the Son and of the Holy Ghost." He felt warm and comfortable in the blankets. He also felt very sleepy. "Good night, Francis, my son." His mother kissed him. He was asleep.

There was a picture near his bed that Francis came gradually to associate in some dim manner with the rite of bedtime. It made a bright gleam of color amid the dingy old portraits of bygone kings and knights of Navarre that covered the walls of the nursery. The picture was a small oil painting of a woman dressed in a flowing robe. Her hands were outstretched. Her look was heavenward and there was a serenity on her face as fresh as the morning. She had roses at her feet and a halo over her head. Francis was not sure that he knew who she was, but he was glad she was there.

2

He felt strangely comforted by her presence. He seldom looked consciously at the picture but sometimes he fancied that the picture was looking at him. He usually found himself being put to bed with the same formula. He did not feel very lonesome after his mother tucked him in and left him. He seemed to feel that somebody was still with him, although he did not know just how or who. He was not afraid of the dark. He felt completely protected in his own little bed.

The age of toddling and romping was not slow in coming to Francis, nor was he slow in doing his full share of both from daylight to dark. If there was an odd corner to poke his nose in, he would find it, and if there was something going on in any place, he was sure to be there. There were many odd corners in the sprawling old castle, and his chief occupation was to roam the big house—and sometimes the big outside garden—on adventure bent. That was how he came upon Father Castro on the morning of the first of May. Scuffling sounds coming from the chapel were enough to prompt him to investigate. He found the rotund chaplain in the act of fastening a paper angel on the drapery around the big statue near the altar. He stopped to survey the operation. Father Castro stopped to survey him.

"Panchito! You are just the man I need to help me," said the priest. "We are fixing up things for the Blessed Mother. Today she is the Queen of Navarre. Let me see." The priest considered. Glad to see his young friend, he was equally anxious to get rid of him. "I know what you can do. Go out in the garden and pick some flowers. Get nice ones. Ask your mother. We must have plenty of flowers today for the Blessed Mother."

Francis left with his commission. He did not see his

mother in the hallway, so he trotted out into the morning sunshine of the garden. Sometimes he found her on the bench with her prayer book and her sewing. He stretched up to his full height and peeked over the little hedge. There she was sitting in her favorite nook over near the bed of rose bushes. He was relieved. He hurried over to her.

Doña Maria closed her book and listened to his story. It was not very coherent, but she understood it. She smiled. Her eyes seemed very bright. She seemed to whisper to herself for a moment. She bent over him and looked into his eyes.

"Flowers for the Blessed Mother, my son? Why, of course." She leaned closer to him. "You know, I want to tell you something, Francis. You belong to the Blessed Mother. I gave you to her when you were a little baby — when you were born."

He screwed up his face in a frown. He looked puzzled. "You gave me, Mother? Don't I belong to you any more?" His lip quivered.

He felt his mother's arm go around him. He heard words that reassured him. "Of course, you belong to me, Son. You will always belong to me. Only you belong to the Blessed Mother also. We all belong to her. She is the Mother of God. And we are all her children. So that's why we bring flowers to her — to honor God's Mother. Now you understand, don't you?"

The mention of flowers brought Francis back to pressing realities. He forgot his trouble and his face brightened. He became the man of action again. His eye fell on a cluster of early roses that were just beginning to bloom. The pink buds looked inviting. He scrambled off the seat and ran to them.

He seized a stalk and gave a pull. The same instant he felt a sharp pain in the palm of his hand. He opened his hand and saw a little bead of red blood on it. He was too surprised to cry. He ran back to his mother.

"Now we'll take it out, Francis. Hold still a minute. It won't hurt you; it's just a little thorn. Don't cry now." The thorn came out and his mother wiped the little jewel of blood off his hand. She did not kiss the spot. She looked earnestly at him. "I am glad you did not cry, Francis," she said. "You did it for God's Mother, so you must offer it to her."

Francis finally carried out his commission with the help of his mother, his sister and the castle gardener. The final result was a bouquet of flowers almost as big as himself. Doña Maria had gone into the chapel to say a quiet prayer when Francis struggled in with his load. She watched him come in. Father Castro was still busy with his decorations around the statue of the Blessed Virgin. She saw Francis toddle up to the priest and hand him the armful of flowers. "For God's Mother," he said. Then she heard the patter of little feet as he turned and tripped out. The Lady of Xavier tarried a moment and said another prayer. In it she offered her son to the Queen of Heaven again. She knew she had forged another link in the compact. She was well satisfied with the toddling of her youngest son.

INITIATION

"PANGE lingua gloriosi!" The fresh, sweet treble rose haltingly, trembled an instant, then swelled out clearly on the high note, and died away in a faint little contralto hush.

Doña Maria smiled in her heart as she listened to the clear little pipe of her youngest son, and the recollection came that no other sounds had ever had power to charm her sensibilities so much as the music of the children's voices. "Like a tiny cascade of rippling water," she mused. "Like leaves falling softly in the forest." She smiled at her own poetic fancies. "Like a little echo of paradise where they came from," her train of thought continued. And then, because her mind was never very far from God, she found herself slipping into an instinctive prayer: "And whither they are going, with Your help," she ended. "Lord, keep them close to Yourself in life and in death. That is their mother's prayer."

The procession wound around the flower-strewn chapel, as the bevy of young girls backed slowly down the aisle. In their billowy white dresses they looked so much alike that she could scarcely distinguish her own daughter from the young servants and retainers who completed the group. The thought came that this common leveling of her big household was fitting for this occasion, since it reduced people and things to the way they really were in the actual sight of God.

Doña Maria thrilled with pride again as the clear voices of her three young sons soared out in the Eucharistic hymn. And now she bowed low as the heavy footfalls of the gardener and the head groom signaled that the canopy was approaching. They walked with solemn dignity, clenching the uprights as if they were supporting the whole world. Under the silken tassels came Father Castro, with fixed eyes that looked neither to right nor left, as he bore before him the Light of the World. She bowed lower as her heart told her that Jesus of Nazareth was passing by, and she breathed another little prayer; if only she might touch the hem of His garment, she knew that all would be well with herself and hers. She felt a thrill of gratitude, too, as she thought of the happy household that the Divine Visitor would find assembled to greet Him. Children, retainers, servants, even visitors, all were there; and all hearts were united in their welcome to the Eucharistic King. It was Holy Week at the Castle of Xavier.

Her mood held during lunch, and she was only half attentive to the sallies of her cousin and his lady, who had come all the way from Madrid to spend Easter in the mountain castle. Don Alvarez was a trusted adviser of the King, and one of the most highly respected men at court, but he had his little weakness, a strong dose of worldliness. There were some who explained that he had imbibed the tendency from his good wife, who was well-known to be endowed with a plentiful supply of it. Yet in any case, he ran that estimable lady a poor second in respect to this dubious characteristic, for his was merely the childish outlook that loved the world and its pleasures, while hers was the slavish mentality that esteemed and courted the world and its absurdities. Not that the fair and gracious Doña Isabella lacked her own good qualities of mind and heart, for of such she had many. Everybody knew her as a woman of many long prayers and much sentimental religiosity. She possessed a kind heart and wished no real harm to anybody. For the rest, she had a mind gifted enough to learn French and to excel in music, although she devoted her mental energies largely to such intellectual pursuits as choosing the right fork and hobnobbing with the right people. The good creature also had a great gift of chatter.

Doña Maria was a good listener when she was interested, and she tried hard to appear to be one when she was not interested, but she found herself attending with only one little polite corner of her mind to the enthusiastic accounts of the court and its doings, with which she was being regaled by her good cousin and his talkative spouse. She felt she should catch the ball of conversation that was being thrown at her and attempt to return it, so she decided to make a little contribution. "Michael and John will be going soon, you know," she offered. "I don't know how much of the court they will see, as they will be under military orders all the time, but anyhow, it is the service of the King."

"They will see plenty," exclaimed Don Alvarez, awakened to a new enthusiasm in his subject by this innocent remark, which represented politeness rather than information, since everybody already knew the future plans of the two young soldiers. "Military orders!" he shouted jovially. "What's that? Think we let that interfere with more important affairs in Madrid? My dear lady, the young officers are the life of the court! Why, I remember when I first went up as a

cadet — what times we had!" He was off on a flood of remi-
niscence, and his smiling audience could only compose themselves to listen.

Meanwhile, all were wondering how the good man was
ever going to find time to eat anything, since he had not yet
interrupted himself long enough to touch the first course,
while the others were already several laps ahead in the program. All, that is, except Doña Isabella, who knew exactly
what to do in the circumstances. With a skill and dexterity
known only to her kind, that adroit lady had already managed to talk even more than her husband, while keeping up
with the procession of dishes at the same time. She appeared
scarcely ever to stop chattering, and yet a glance at her plate
invariably revealed that its contents had been efficiently dis-
patched in some apparently miraculous manner. A look at
her hostess told her that it was time to direct the energies of
Don Alvarez into a more useful channel, whereupon she
promptly took the lead away from him, so that he might
turn some attention to his plate.

Doña Isabella gave her own version of the attractions and
distractions of life at court, conveying the rather contradic-
tory impression that a much-sought-after person like herself
found it all very boring, and at the same time that no other
life was worth living. She had a word to say about the young
officers also, and from it one might have gathered that there
was a time — and that not so long ago — when the chief
occupation of these young men had been to see who could
stand highest in her own favor and estimation. This disconcerted Don Alvarez no whit, except to call up to his mind
a mild and not altogether unpleasurable speculation as to how
different life might have been if one of them had succeeded

in these largely imagined aspirations. He knew his treasure, however, and had long become resigned to the little deficiencies that went with it. He entertained no very disloyal regrets as he continued to make up his arrears in the food and to beam expansively upon the company.

"And when is Francis going?" pursued Doña Isabella brightly, after a series of sallies intended by the kind-hearted creature to dazzle and compliment Michael and John. She turned to the youngest boy, who had been gravely and politely taking in everything in the way of both food and conversation. "He will be at home there. He has the air of the court already," she continued, looking at the refined little face peeping out from the velvet collar. The third son was built on a slightly more delicate mold than his elder brothers, and his compact little frame wore an air of boyish dignity.

Francis looked at his mother, but that wise lady held her peace. He wore a puzzled frown as he replied to his questioner. "I don't know, Doña Isabella. I don't know if anybody wants me there," he faltered. "Or, even if I want to go there," he added hastily. His little mind was undergoing a slight disturbance of which he was not completely conscious. The glowing prospect held out for Michael and John did not attract him in itself, but neither did the thought that it was something from which destiny might have excluded him. The boy turned to his plate, but the little frown of thought clung to him.

Father Castro noted this little byplay, but if he had any opinion on the subject under discussion, he did not make it known. Besides, he was intent on another matter of his own. As soon as the meal was over, he started out to recruit

10

the members of the household as watchers before the Blessed Sacrament. He had not been long about it before he saw Francis sidling over in his direction.

"May I watch an hour, too, Father?" asked the boy in a small, shy voice. He fidgeted a little, blushed one minute, and the next looked elaborately unconcerned.

Father Castro regarded his petitioner with an air of open-eyed surprise that was somewhat discounted by a poorly disguised smile. "What!" he exclaimed. "Watch an hour? Keep still for sixty minutes by the clock? Well, if you can, it will surprise me. You can't be climbing trees and riding ponies in the chapel, remember."

"Father, you are only fooling," said the boy. He looked out the window, shifted uneasily. "I don't ride ponies when I serve Mass for you, do I?"

The priest found this a good answer. He completely reversed his tactics. "Well then, how will you keep awake?" he objected. "An hour is a very long time for a very small boy. You will fall asleep in the middle of it, I'll be bound!"

Francis was persistent. "But I don't always fall asleep in chapel, Father," he replied. "The days you come to say Mass, I try hard to keep awake because I know that God is there in the tabernacle." He paused, and then delivered an unconscious clincher. "Would God be angry if I fell asleep, Father?" He asked the question in all innocence.

Father Castro laughed and patted the boy's shoulder. This broadside had completely undermined him. "Not very angry, my son," he said. "He would not be very angry; that's a fact. All right. I give you five to six. That is about the time Our Lord began the Agony in the Garden. You can watch an hour with Him."

11

A little boy knelt before the Repository and made his little prayer. What he said or thought he did not know. In the solemn hush his eyes wandered over the altar with its flickering candles and silken draperies that told of the Presence there. Sometimes he felt a little rush of thanksgiving because God was so close. Sometimes his fancy strayed to a distant garden where he saw a kneeling figure that seemed somehow not so very far away. Sometimes he thought of his mother and brothers and sisters, and he prayed for blessings on them all. For a long time he only knelt and looked at the tabernacle with no thought at all. No thought? He was merely not conscious of it. For all the time his soul was echoing a prayer that had broken from the lips of a great apostle many years ago. The little heart was thinking and saying nothing, but it was feeling with every beat: "Lord, it is good for us to be here."

So the long hour passed — only it did not seem so very long. And the boy did not fall asleep — only nodded and cat-napped a very few times; although it is also true that he found very little in all this time to say to God. But it may be that God found a great deal to say to him.

Francis said nothing to Don Alvarez and Doña Isabella. He said nothing to Father Castro. He said nothing to himself. But when he was going to bed, he said something to his mother, apropos of nothing at all. "Mother," he said, "I don't think I want to go to court." And his mother said nothing. She only smiled. But it was a beautiful smile, something like the smile of angels when there is rejoicing in heaven.

N a CASTLE GARDEN

IT was the time of golden grain and the languorous enchainment of late summer lay upon the fruitful fields where they stretched out basking motionless in the sun. The rasp of a thousand dog-day cicadas droned away. In the green wood along the slope all was still. Save for the occasional chirp of an irrepressible chickadee, the feathered people had left off their customary twittering to drowse away the hot hours in the universal siesta that had apparently enveloped living things. In the Spanish garden no sounds were heard save the soft plashing of the fountain and the whispering of the bees in the holly-hocks. Even here it was hot — up the airy mountain where the Castle of Xavier spread its ramparts to look down upon the smiling valley of Navarre.

Only Madeline could not sleep. The nervousness inciden-tal to her recent homecoming was not yet dissipated. It had been intensified on this occasion by the impending of an announcement — to her of major importance — which she had resolved to make to the family. She gave up the attempt to sleep, and opening the casement stepped into the garden to seek a favorite nook where a rustic bench looked out from its curtain of heavily sweet lilac on the valley below.

To her surprise it had already been claimed by a rare occu-pant. Fourteen-year-old brothers were seldom found quietly dreaming on a bench, even in sixteenth-century Navarre.

"Well, my young philosopher," said Madeline, taking a seat beside the family's youngest member, "what has made you so quiet all of a sudden? I am glad your poor pony is getting a rest for once, anyhow. Well, it's nice to be young. I wish I were fourteen again instead of being grown up and having to go and live in that silly old court. You'd be surprised, Francis. The people are nice but the life is so false. Everything is ceremony and fussing, and nobody really enjoys it. From the Queen down we are all kept busy saying things we don't mean and doing things we don't see any sense in. It's all show. I'm sick of it."

"That's funny, Madeline," replied the boy slowly. "I was just sort of thinking the same thing in a way. Not about you, but about things in general. I've often thought I'd like to go to court and see if I could amount to something there. And I often think it would be nice to be a soldier, like Michael and John, and fight for Navarre. But sometimes I wonder what the use of it is, after all. And sometimes I think it's better to be a priest like Father Castro and say Mass and try to help lots of people, or something like that." He stopped, surprised, even a trifle embarrassed at having said so much.

"Why, Francis, are you serious?"

"I don't know; I was just kind of thinking like that," he replied, resuming the small boy's guard against anything approaching heart-to-heart confidences.

"Francis," said Madeline with a sudden resolve, "I'm going to tell you something. Maybe it's right to tell you first on account of your beautiful name. It is the name of the little poor man of Assisi. Well, I am going to be one of his daughters. That's why I came home. I am not going back to

14

court. I am going to join the Poor Clares in Gandia. Isn't that wonderful?"

"Yes, it is, Madeline," at once replied the boy. "It's much better than going to court. Living in God's house is the best of all. I'm glad."

She looked at the suddenly eager young face. The boy was old enough to know what a vocation was. That innocent little heart had experienced nothing but the sheltered life of the Castle, and in its chapel had passed the happiest moments it had known. What wonder if the dew of divine grace had found there also a fruitful soil? The interested look of the boy impressed Madeline, but she did not wish to venture a direct question.

Her gaze wandered out over the valley where the fields shimmered bright with grain. A thought came to her. "Look, Francis," she said, suddenly. "Look at the fields ready for the harvest. Do you remember how Our Lord pointed them out to the Apostles? He said the harvest was great and the laborers were few. There is much work to do for Him. His harvest is saving souls, you know."

"Yes, I know," said the boy. His eyes rested on the summer fields spread out before them. He was silent a moment. "I know what Our Lord meant," he added simply. "But, of course, Madeline, I do not know if it is my vocation."

"Well," smiled Madeline, "don't worry. God will make it known to you in due time." She arose. "I think it's about time for Mother to wake up from her siesta, and I want to go in and tell her my news. You say a prayer for me, Francis, and I'll pray for you. May God direct us both."

The lady of the Castle was up and bustling about her household duties when Madeline returned to the house, nor was she greatly surprised to learn from her daughter's lips the story of her vocation. "God be praised, my daughter, for this great grace," was the way she greeted the announce- ment. "It is the greatest honor that could come to our house. Far better than for you to serve at an earthly court. To think that God has chosen one of my own for His service. I give you to Him freely. May He be forever blessed."

"And mother," added Madeline, relieved and elated to the point of immediate self-forgetfulness by the consoling, even though fully expected, answer, "I may be wrong and perhaps I ought not to mention it, but I have an idea that Francis may also have a vocation. Just now we were talking in the garden . . ."

"Did he say so?"

"No," replied Madeline. "He only acted as if his thoughts were drifting that way."

"What did he say?"

"It wasn't the words on his lips; it was the light in his eyes. We were speaking of the religious life. Of course, it's too soon to tell. I just thought I'd mention it to you."

"Well," replied the mother, "we have sometimes thought Francis might be a priest. That would be the summit of my happiness. In fact, I have been rather hoping for it — at least in my dreams and prayers. If he shows the inclina- tion when the time comes, I will make any sacrifice to pro- vide for him. Don't worry, Madeline. Only pray that God will make us worthy of these great blessings."

Seven years later Madeline had long been a full-fledged Poor Clare and one noted for holiness of life even in that community of model religious. Never had she forgotten to pray for the young brother whose demeanor had impressed

16

her so strangely on the announcement of her own vocation. And Francis had in the main lived up to the hopes she entertained of him.

His twenty-first birthday found him a student at the University of Paris. In those days there were few seminaries; and students of all classes flocked to the universities, where they sometimes found — and sometimes lost — their vocations. Francis had seemed to have a vocation, and two years previously his mother had insisted that he be allowed to go and make the necessary studies. This was done at a great sacrifice. The family fortunes were at a very low ebb. Much of their estates had been confiscated in the wars; and Michael, the oldest son, who ever since his father's death had been the head of the house, was hard put to it to keep up a semblance of solvency. Yet the mother gained her point. Francis had a vocation, and Francis must study, no matter what the sacrifice.

At first all had gone well, but recently the situation had become disquieting. Times had grown increasingly hard, and the added expense more difficult to meet. On top of this there began to filter home an impression of Francis' lack of seriousness at the University. He was always a brilliant student. His time was not wasted. But his vocation? He was apparently running with a gay crowd and his appeals for money became more and more frequent. Finally, Michael and John felt it was time to call a halt.

"Mother," said Michael, "don't you think we shall have to recall Francis? It's not certain that he will be a priest; in fact, from the rumors I hear about him, he seems to be tending the other way. And it's almost impossible to meet the expense. Here we are scraping desperately to hold together what is left of the estate, and hard put to it at times to keep the hands in the fields, or even to feed and clothe ourselves decently, while that young gentleman runs around Paris and keeps writing home for money. I think it would be better for him to come home and become a soldier like the rest of us."

"My son, it is not certain that Francis has no vocation," replied the gentle mother. "I still think he has one. Yet, I am also worried about the reports we hear of him. We are far from Paris, and it is hard to judge. But, of course, the money is a great difficulty. If we simply haven't got it, then I suppose we shall have to think of bringing him home. Yet, it will break my heart almost. Isn't there some other way?"

"Well, I don't see any," returned Michael gloomily. "Of course, it's physically possible to get enough money for his bare expenses and keep him there, if you insist on it. Only it's very hard — and the worst of it is, it seems useless. It may turn out to be simply throwing it away."

The mother hesitated. Michael had all the reason on his side. And he had worked so hard and sacrificed so much to keep up the family that it did seem an imposition to ask him to do more. "Will my little Francis never be a priest after all?" she wondered. Suddenly a straw of an idea floated across her consciousness, and she clutched at it. It was a memory of Madeline on a sunny afternoon years before, telling of her own happiness in her heaven-sent vocation and then adding her conviction — a little fancifully she had thought at the time — of a like grace being in store for her little brother.

She turned to Michael. "Well, my son, this is a matter

we must not decide lightly. The question of a vocation to the priesthood affects who knows how many immortal souls," she said, unconsciously prophetic in the case of this smiling young son of hers whose conquests for Christ were later to prove as the sands of the sea in number. "In a matter of this kind, suppose we write first to your sister Madeline and find out what she thinks. I am resigned to the will of God in the affair; let us only take all possible means to find it out. Madeline is a holy Sister, and it is only fitting that we consult her on this question. She may even have some special light from God."

"Why, certainly, Mother; anything you say," replied the excellent but sorely tried Michael. "It will give us more light to get Madeline's advice. I only want to do what is right. Let us see what Madeline says and then decide."

Duly the letter went to the holy Poor Clare in her convent at Gandia. To her the message brought the memory of a last visit home and a little boy looking out from the lilac arbor over a valley filled with billowing grain. She did not answer the letter at once, however. She went to the chapel and there she spoke to God. And there, doubtless, God spoke to her. For she then sat down in haste and penned this answer:

> "I beseech you, do not take this step. On the contrary, provide for the studies of my brother Francis at any sacrifice. I am possessed of a certitude that he will become a great servant of God and the instrument of salvation to many souls."

The response was too decisive to fail in resolving Michael's doubts. The boy stayed at the University. And the dream — or perhaps it was a vision — of a brother and sister in their sunkissed Spanish garden came true eventually in God's vast field afar, for the vocation was that of Francis Xavier.

INIGO'S MIRACLE

A COLD wind rattled through the long cloister that bisected the whole length of the College of Saint Barbara. The students rubbed their hands and shivered, as they hurried along between the cold, gray walls. Merry faces predominated, however, in the throng that came trooping by twos and threes, most of whom were in some kind of animated conversation. Heads were thrown back in sudden laughter, as jokes and near jokes were retailed here and there, after the eternal fashion of schoolboys to whom the only unforgivable crime is to be serious. Some romped and pantomimed, while others wheeled about to greet companions with boisterous exclamations.

It was November in Paris several centuries before the introduction of steam heat. The boys did not miss it. The animal spirits of their hardy generation rendered such coddling superfluous. Besides, they were on their way to supper in the big, vaulted refectory, where the crusty loaves and red wine of France would soon fortify the inner man to withstand the chill.

A man with the hard-bitten face of the ascetic entered the refectory, sat down nodding to those around him, ate sparingly of one dish, drank off a glass of wine and water, and folded his napkin. Next to him was seated a younger man, whose delicate features and gentle expression combined to give that appearance which men have agreed to call angelic.

21

The more mature man turned to his younger companion, who had finished his own scanty meal with equal dispatch. "Peter Favre," he said banteringly, his stern face relaxing and a sudden kindness softening his piercing black eyes, "you are not eating enough! How will you ever do any work for God, if you begin by starving to death? It isn't always Lent. Keep your body strong, or you'll regret it. I have been through all that. A man's body is miserable enough at best, without adding ill health to make it worse."

The young man smiled at the little tirade. "Your words would carry greater weight, if you gave better example," he said slyly. "I'll engage to pamper the body just as much as my worthy preceptor does," he finished with a mock bow.

The two men smiled a smile of mutual understanding, but the younger man's face immediately clouded, as his mind reverted to a preoccupation that he had wished, and yet feared, to speak about. "Inigo," he said, turning on his companion, "are you not worried about Francis? I've wanted to speak to you for some time. I think his success is going to his head. Since he went to Beauvais College, you know."

"I shouldn't wonder," replied the older man a little dryly. "But what can we do about it?" he asked with a bit of a gentle smile.

"Well, no offense now. But here's what I wanted to say. With Francis spoiled already by his little success, do you think it is wise to add to it? I admit he is a first-rate philosopher, but you know perfectly well he would not have scored such a big success so soon, if you had not gone out of your way to send him students. Now they are all flocking to him, and it's not doing him any good. When a man is full of pride and vanity already, why not leave bad enough alone?"

Peter Favre stopped, breathless after his long outburst, and wondering how it would be received. He was relieved to see the older man still smiling.

"The point is well taken, Peter," came the answer. "I admit I am playing a hazardous game. But the stake is worth it. And I've studied my man a bit, you know. Unless I am entirely wrong, he is too genuine at bottom to be fooled long by a little success. Or even by a big one. The sooner he succeeds, the sooner he will see the futility of succeeding. Some men would be spoiled, I grant you. But a generous nature is won best by generosity. That's Francis. And that's my plan." Inigo sighed. He was far from feeling the assurance he expressed. He turned to Favre with a great earnestness. "What I really count upon, Peter, are your prayers. That is what wins these battles. Pray much. We shall win yet, if it is God's will."

Well-fed boys began to file out of the refectory. Knots of them gathered here and there, making plans to spend their evening in the various haunts of Paris. The two companions rose and joined the stream that soon issued on the street. A constitutional walk was their custom.

They had not gone very far when a voice from the crowd hailed them. They looked around to see a man approaching, young enough to be a student, but wearing the doctor's cape that proclaimed the teacher. In his piquant face danced snapping black eyes. The young man was quite unconscious that he had so recently been the object of their solicitude.

They chatted a bit, walking along. The newcomer was bound for a night out, and was looking for companions. According to him, a lot of fun was going to be had at some party which he was attending. "There are some clever men

23

coming," he said, "and we shall discuss everything under the sun. Perhaps a few more, besides. A man must hear all sides these days. It makes a full mind." The enthusiastic and sententious professor paused for encouragement.

"Much more likely to make a full skin, I should think," replied the more mature Inigo, who had attended a few such gatherings and knew that they promised anything but intellectual advancement. He turned and bestowed a large and solemn wink on Peter Favre.

Favre suddenly decided that he was in a hurry to go somewhere. "If you will excuse me, I'll just chase along," he said abruptly. "Piles of work to do. See you later." He was off, leaving the other two to stroll on alone.

The young professor was no whit abashed by these dashes of cold water, and he kept up a lively chatter about parties and a number of other things. Inigo listened, throwing in a word of patient interest now and again. He wanted to earn attention by first giving it. Finally the younger man got to the end of his talk about the boyish dreams and fantastic plans that characterize the unreality of a university world. He closed on the apologetic note characteristic of those who sponsor the heady idealisms of youth, while retaining a little too much sense to believe in them completely themselves. "Of course, none of us knows much, after all. I shall never invent a new philosophy. I shall be lucky if I can keep on dealing out enough Aristotle to hold my job. Still it's fun to try."

The older man suddenly turned on him, standing stock-still. His eyes pierced, while his hand arrested, his young companion. "Francis! Suppose you did discover a new system, as you call it. What would it mean beyond the praises of a few empty heads? Suppose the greatest success you can imagine. What would it do for you except to expose you to the one great danger, which is pride? What does it profit a man if he gain the whole world, and suffer the loss of his own soul?"

The professor listened to him, because he could not well do otherwise. But his gorge rose. He wished he were capable of being coldly rude. Instead he stiffened a bit, and replied with a trace of irritation. "I thought that was coming. But don't go so fast, if you please. You speak as if I were on the high road to perdition, or something. What is the idea of preaching a sermon at me on the public street? This is the second time. Really, Inigo, you must have constituted yourself spiritual adviser to the whole university. Yet I, for one, do not recall choosing you in that capacity." He paused. Wishing to repel, he hesitated to offend. There was little danger. Inigo only laughed.

"There is justice in what you say, Francis. However, out of the whole university, you are the only one to whom I have spoken in this particular way. Think that over." Inigo patted his companion on the back. "Well, go ahead to your party. I must get along, too, to puzzle my old head over what Tacitus said about the Germans." With a smile and a wave of the hand, he was off.

It was a few weeks later when Inigo got his revenge. The three men shared the same quarters. They were all bending over the books one evening, when Francis received a letter from home. He frowned as he read it; he put it away, and kept on frowning. He did some thinking along practical, rather than philosophical lines. Then he rose, and approached

Inigo. "Private matter, my old one," he said in a low voice. "Could I speak to you a moment?"

Inigo rose and accompanied him into the hall, wondering a little.

"It's this way," said Francis, coming straight to the point. "I need some money. I just got a letter from home, but there was nothing in it. I don't quite understand, because I wrote for it. Anyhow, it leaves me in a bit of a fix. I owe some here and there, you know. And I've got to do a little entertaining. And—"

"How much do you need?" came the answer from the older man, without the least hesitation. "What is mine is yours. Say the word."

A little later Francis, with Inigo's loan in his pocket, was on the street, headed for an evening out. Inigo returned to the books. He read a bit, but felt Peter Favre's eyes boring into his back. He closed his book, and turned to his companion. "I suppose you took in the latest act in this little comedy of ours, Peter," he said, a trifle defensively.

"I couldn't help hearing a few sentences," replied Peter. "Have it your own way, of course. But I am not at all sure that was wise. On top of everything else you lend him money to continue his foolish running around. More vanity, that's all. What possible good can that do?"

"It can help to show him the vanity of vanities, perhaps," said Inigo, in no wise disconcerted. He turned fully around. "Seriously, Peter, you know my theory about Francis. I want to bind him by the chords of Adam. I know that gratitude is the rarest of virtues, but you must also remember that we are dealing with the rarest of men. Let him once wake up to realities, and you will see a return of my investment. It is for your prayers to wake him up, that's all. Stick to that, Peter, will you please?" continued Inigo gently, but firmly. "And let me handle the human element in my own blundering way."

For a month they saw little of Francis, except when he returned late at night from some meeting or other to drop into bed exhausted. With all his gaiety, however, the young professor was looking worried. He received some money from home, and paid back his loan with expressions of gratitude. But this time he did not blossom out in new clothes, nor go in for the other extravagances customary to students in general and to Francis in particular. Actually the letter from home had sobered him a bit. Along with the money, there was a rather serious warning from his eldest brother to indicate that the house of Xavier was getting tired of financing student prodigality. The letter made him think.

Other circumstances likewise combined to give him pause. The philosophy class that had been a pure delight was beginning to reveal to its young teacher the many bizarre opinions bandied about by his students and confreres. He grudgingly admitted to himself that many views, tenaciously held and recklessly advocated by his friends, were unquestionably heretical and indefensible. He was himself a man of an intellect at once penetrating and bold; but the mere wildness of an idea was not enough to interest his well-balanced mind, whereas this shady recommendation alone apparently sufficed to attract his equally bold, but less intelligent, companions.

Of late his usually complacent thoughts about the future had undergone a mysterious disturbance. Gradually taking shape in his mind was a yet indistinct ideal of sacrifice, that began imperceptibly to replace his former enthusiasms. His projected career of a comfortable existence spiced with scholastic éclat took on the aspect of an insipid ambition that suddenly did not seem to matter. Born in him somehow was a vague but growingly insistent desire for something higher, better, costing more. "Costing more?" he asked himself one time. "No, costing everything." He wanted no half-measures. His still unanalyzed thoughts played about a central notion of burning bridges, committing oneself, going the whole way. Soon he began to know what ambition could really mean, as the new appeal gained distinctness and force. He wanted to live dangerously — and for a great cause. He did not yet pronounce the word, but what he wanted was sacrifice.

At the outset his guard was up, and thoughts like these stole in only at odd moments. At first they met with hasty dismissal, then with shy entertainment, and gradually with hesitating acceptance. He noticed that the more he gave himself up to them, the happier he became. At times the mere yielding of his will to the now dominating train of thought flooded him with an overwhelming joy. "I will give all," he finally discovered himself answering to the insistent question now ringing in his heart.

If Inigo had any knowledge of all this, he did not display it. He met Francis seldom, and then with a cool insouciance. He was not worried. When he had planted a seed, he knew it needed time to germinate. Besides, was not that angelic Peter Favre storming heaven with his prayers? Inigo was content to wait.

The end was not long delayed. Inigo was studying one evening when Francis came in, looking rather serious. Francis hesitated. Inigo looked at him, saw something in his eyes, sensed something in his demeanor. Inigo laid down his book, yawned, stretched. "What's on your mind?" he asked casually. "Did you discover a new system of philosophy? Or did you find the answer to my question?"

"Both," smiled Francis. "Your question is the only philosophy, after all!" He squared around, serious, intent, appealing. "Inigo! Tell me what to do."

The older man stood up, placed his hands on Francis' shoulders, and looked in his eyes. "Do you want to throw in your lot with me, Francis? It isn't going to be easy. It may lead us to Calvary, you know."

"That's all right," said Francis simply. "Inigo, if it's to the end of the world, it doesn't matter to me."

Years later the Spanish used to say that while Xavier worked many miracles and Ignatius only one, yet that one was greater than all of Xavier's, for that one miracle was Xavier himself.

THE RUNNER LOSES

SAINT IGNATIUS sent his first band of recruits to preach in Italy. They had to spend weary weeks of hiking down through Savoy and over the lower Alps. They started in high spirits. They were young, and they were setting out to win a world for Christ. They felt like flying, but they soon ran into an un-expected difficulty. They found themselves slowing up.

"What's the matter with Father Xavier?" asked Simon Rodriguez on the third day out. "He seems to have a hard time keeping up with us. Strange! I should have thought he would outstrip all of us. The famous runner of Saint Barbara, you know."

The next day was a stern march. The rocky road wound down valleys and over mountain passes in a seemingly never-ending ribbon. The distance was longer than usual to the only habitable inn that offered a night's lodging. Francis Xavier seemed to have hard going. He lagged behind re-peatedly. Peter Favre was openly worried and questioned him repeatedly. The whole party now shared his anxiety. To the solicitude of all Francis returned a smile and a shake of the head. He stumbled on.

Never did an inn look so good to the weary travelers as that night. They were all footsore, stiff, spent. Francis hobbled in last. He was deathly pale. He staggered to a seat beside Peter Favre and sat down. He leaned over to whisper in Favre's ear. "My feet," he said, and slid to the ground. He had fainted.

When they had revived him and got his shoes off, they ceased to wonder. His legs were swollen enormously and black with congested blood.

"What on earth!" exclaimed Peter Favre. Then he looked closer and understood. Just above the ankle of each foot was a depression. Obviously something was tied around his legs, so tightly as to cause the flesh on both sides practically to close over it.

"Better get a doctor," suggested Simon Rodriguez. "So that's what happened to the runner! Some more of Xavier's rashness. He can't do anything by halves, not even when it comes to serving God. Less zeal and more sense is what he needs." His laugh ended in a sigh, "I'd give all my sense, though, for half his zeal."

The doctor found that Xavier had tied ropes around his legs but he was nonplussed as to how to get them off. The flesh had closed up over the cords so that it was impossible to insert a knife to cut them. "Wait till tomorrow," he advised. "I'll treat his legs and try to help him get some sleep. In the morning I can see better how to relieve him."

That night Peter Favre got even less sleep than the tossing, restless patient. He was worried about his friend. "What a rash piece of business," he thought with some little asperity. "Could ruin the whole trip and maim him for life." Then he smiled. "Yet how typical," he mused on. "Just like him!" The remark of Simon Rodriguez came back to him. That was the key. His thoughts turned to the past. The old scenes flooded over him. He was back in the early student days at Saint Barbara. He gave up the idea of sleeping. He

31

arose and stepped out into the quiet night air. He paced up and down, letting his memories take possession of him. One scene was vividly etched on his mind. He lived it over again.

"On your mark — ready — go!" He saw again the eager pack of boys go flashing down the college yard. For thirty yards the score or so of youngsters were clinging together in a confused jumble. He remembered what an odd assort-ment of boys they were — all ages and sizes and no two dressed alike.

Suddenly a slim young form had shot out from the mass. Almost as if in one bound the young runner had put five yards of daylight between himself and the ruck. His flying legs were working like pistons in that undeviating precision that proclaims the sprinter.

"The Spanish student looks like a runner," somebody had remarked on the sidelines. "Looks like a runner!" exclaimed another. "Believe me, that boy is a runner — look at that stride! Martin Tour had better watch his laurels. That youngster is flying."

"Wait a minute," somebody added. "He hasn't won this race yet. That blue shirt on the outside is going to give him a tussle."

Another figure had emerged from the group — a tall French boy with long legs. He was putting out everything he had in an effort to catch the flying Spaniard. Slowly he gained. At the thirty-yard mark he drew abreast. As he did so the Spanish boy turned his head slightly in apparent sur-prise, and the next minute was bounding away in a spurt that left his rival as if he were standing still. He crossed the tape yards ahead of the challenger, who was again sepa-

32

rated by yards from the rest. The young Spaniard, a new-comer at Saint Barbara, had made a runaway out of his first race. Peter recalled his own pleasure. The new student was his roommate. It was the first time he had ever seen Francis Xavier run a race. He had said nothing about his interest in racing. Peter liked his modesty.

In the sixteenth century, boys went to school mainly to study; and there was no such thing as collegiate rivalry in games. The students played among themselves, however, and at the University of Paris at least the emulation thus excited had developed to the point of interclass contests. The interclass race was always something of a little event. It was usually held toward the end of the year, after all the various class races had been run off and everybody had a good idea of who was who.

Favre remembered that race. That year it had aroused even more than the usual attention. Francis Xavier had gone on winning races right and left. There were several men in other classes who loomed up as serious contenders. Then there was Martin Tour. Could anybody beat him? That had been the question. Yet this year there was to be some real opposition. At least it would be a race, not a runaway. Interest ran high.

Practically the whole school had been there when the great morning came and the boys sauntered out on the field. This time they were dressed in proper uniforms, short and light and designed for running. There was Martin Tour lolling about the starting line, smiling, confident, a trifle bored. Winning races was an old story to him. Most of the other boys danced around a bit and joked spasmodically to relieve keyed-up nerves. The quietest of all the boys was the self-contained but tense young Spaniard. Francis Xavier had never lost a race yet, but neither had he ever engaged in such a formidable one.

"Well, let's get going," shouted the master of ceremonies, one of the senior boys.

This time the eight boys, all picked runners, got off like one man, except for Martin. He was so used to winning races that he did not bother to strain for the split-second advantage. It was to prove a mistake. Instead of passing the crowd easily he was obliged to put out all he had to catch them at the fifty-yard mark. At the sixty he forged ahead slightly. Francis came with him. At the seventy they were neck and neck. Martin was hitting his fastest clip, but he strained every nerve for a spurt. He gained a yard but not for long. He was spent, while the Spanish boy held back the slight reserve that wins races. On the eighty-yard stripe he let go. He caught Martin, passed him. Martin threw himself forward in a despairing lunge, but he could not meet the challenge. A bounding spurt carried Francis out in front, and the next minute he had flashed over the line a yard ahead of Martin Tour. The school had a new champion.

Favre felt comforted as the scenes from the old student days flashed before him. He found himself smiling. "Poor boy," he thought. "Why, he never said a word about his running, even when he was champion. How could a man be more modest? Of course, he might have had his own thoughts about it. Anyhow, God will surely accept his foolish little sacrifice." A relief had come with the crowding memories. Favre began to feel more normal. He thought perhaps he could sleep. "Now if that good doctor can only fix him up tomorrow," he reflected, "we will see that he does not make the same mistake again." He said a prayer. He retraced his steps to the inn.

The next morning a surprised doctor found his work anticipated. In some way the cords had snapped off the legs of the suffering patient during the night, to the great relief of Father Xavier and almost equally of the puzzled doctor.

"Forgive me, Peter," said Francis shamefacedly to Favre when they were alone. "It was on account of winning the races. At school, you know. It was foolish of me, but I had to do something." He smiled. "Well, this is one race I lost anyway," he ended.

Peter Favre smiled also. He decided it was time to give some advice. "Maybe it's the first race you ever really won, Francis," he said dryly. "You learned how not to be a missioner, anyhow. That's something gained. You may need those legs. Remember what Ignatius told us? Don't run at an uncertainty. Run that you may obtain."

THE HOSTLER WINS

A CAVALCADE of mounted men was slowly defiling through a narrow pass in the lower Italian Alps. Most of them were soldiers. In the lead rode an ill-favored, hard-faced man in the dress of an hostler, whose obvious duty it was to pick out the precarious path for the party. At the rear of the procession was a group of a half-dozen men dressed in citizens' clothes. Three of them wore the livery of servants. Two more were dressed in what was the height of fashion in the sixteenth century, for this befitted the stations of the Portuguese Ambassador and his secretary.

The last man's clothes were not worth looking at; but, nobody looked at his clothes, who saw his face. The clothes consisted of a worn black cassock, a flopping hat, and a broken pair of shoes; the face was that reflection of other-worldliness that masked only partially the eager soul of Francis Xavier. Just now it was smiling at the Ambassador, who had half turned in his saddle to shout back at his companion. Francis pressed his horse up a bit, straining to hear. The path was too narrow to ride abreast.

"I was asking if you are not hungry, Padre," shouted the Ambassador over his shoulder. "This famous guide of ours has got us on the wrong path, as usual. Should have reached the inn an hour ago. I think we went wrong on that last turn."

"Does seem a bit long," replied the priest. "Still, what's

the odds? If he made a mistake, it was a fortunate one. Glorious ride. I almost hope he makes some more."

He paused, switching flies from his horse's mane. It was the only use he had for his whip, as a rule. He patted the horse's bobbing neck. The good animal plodded willingly on. He liked his present rider, for he was sure of gentle handling on the road and an extra good feed at the end of it. Here the path was an undulating hem skirting the base of the mountain. Sometimes the riders had to dodge the spreading branches of the trees that overhung the road, and to shake off the vines that clutched at them as they passed along. Through bowers of green they went, and presently clattered through stony brooks, up sudden hillocks, and down precipitate ravines. At times the road narrowed to a mere thread that hugged the steep mountain side and looked down on the gulley below, which stretched away in places steep and sheer enough to become a precipice. If it was a glorious ride, what made it so was the green grandeur of the scenes that framed the road rather than the precarious path itself. The travelers had to pick their way very carefully.

The Ambassador, for his part, had quite enough of both road and scenery, and by the time they had wound through the last defiles and found themselves finally at their belated inn, he was in a bad humor that boded no good to the inefficient guide. He made it his first business to call the delinquent.

Xavier tried to make a diversion by manifesting a sudden interest in food. "Smells good in that kitchen," he beamed at the Ambassador. "Let's hurry up and eat. I'm famished; aren't you?" What he wanted to say was: "Don't make the mistake of giving correction on an empty stomach."

But the Ambassador was not to be denied. He proceeded to administer a royal, or at least an ambassadorial, reprimand to the luckless guide. Xavier busied himself about the baggage. He did not overhear all the conversation, but he sensed that the guide was receiving a very severe dressing-down. The guide said almost nothing, beyond a few mumbled words of excuse. Xavier saw him go out a few minutes later, looking, and apparently thinking, daggers.

Soon the welcome call to supper came. It was not long before the tasty broth and crusty loaves of the mountain inn restored cheerfulness to the party. Or at least to all save one. Xavier, eating sparingly after his wont, noticed the hostler wolfing his food with sullen brow and averted looks. The scolding was rankling in his mind.

It was some hours after, and almost time to go to bed, when Xavier strolled around to the stables to have a look at his horse before turning in. As he passed a group of men in the stable yard, he heard a voice raised in anger. It was the hostler surrounded by a group of soldiers. He was reciting his woes in no uncertain terms. Violent oaths and blasphemies studded his harangue. The soldiers, in no way concerned, were quite content to listen to his grievance. Every man had a right, in their simple code, to air his troubles as he saw fit. Xavier shuddered at some of the vile expressions that assailed his ears. He thought of remonstrating, hesitated, compromised on a prayer, went on. "A sullen, graceless fellow," he mused. "Not easy to appeal to a type of his sort. I shall have to wait for some propitious moment." He went to sleep praying for the unprepossessing sheep that Divine Providence had seen fit to include in his temporary fold.

38

Next morning they took to the saddle bright and early, and this time the guide did not lag along looking for the path, but put off at speed and soon was out of sight. The country was even wilder than that traversed the day before, but by the same token the path was easier to follow, since it was the only one that crossed that almost uninhabited section. Xavier saw his chance. He coaxed his horse to speed up and catch the hostler so that he could utilize this rare opportunity to talk to the man alone. Men do not talk about their souls in a crowd; and it was a question if this one would talk about his soul even out of a crowd. But it was worth trying. The good horse flew along, although the path was tenuous and uneven to the point of danger. Occasionally the horse would slip on a loose rock, but the sure-footed animal managed always to retain his feet, while the stones and debris dislodged by his flying hoofs went clattering down to the gulley below. Xavier was taking risks. Finally, however, the path got so wretched and the declivity below it so steep that he was forced by elementary prudence to slow down to a walk. He was actually on a precipice.

Suddenly he heard a sound. What was that? He stopped and listened. It came again. Was it a moan from somebody in pain? Sounded like it. It seemed to be coming from the foot of the precipice. Xavier got off his horse and looked over the sheer drop. Then he understood. There, stretched out in the scrub bushes at the bottom of the ravine, was the form of a man. A low groan again. Not far from him a horse lay prone. The picture was clear. A hasty rider had gone over the cliff. Xavier shuddered as he instinctively realized how easily the same thing might have happened to himself. But not for long. Action was in order. He tethered his horse to a tree, hitched up his soutane, prepared to make the descent.

It was perilous going, and as he picked his way down, he did not dare to let his mind dwell on the impossible problem of climbing up again with a man on his back. "Maybe the soldiers will have some means," he thought vaguely, as he scrambled along, now getting a foothold on a square inch of jutting rock, again clinging for a necessary instant to some bit of shrubbery, and all the time wondering if the precarious supports would hold his weight. But a boyhood spent in clambering around the mountains and glens of Navarre had prepared him for just such tests as this, and thanks to a wiry frame and a cool head he soon found himself standing by the side of the fallen man.

There a surprise awaited him. Something about the man seemed familiar. "Why, it's our friend, the guide," he ejaculated, as he bent over the motionless form. At once all was plain. "Poor chap," he reflected. "Started out on a helter-skelter ride, disgruntled, discouraged, angry, reckless, devil-may-care." He scooped some water from the tiny rivulet that poured through the gulley. The unconscious man was giving an occasional groan. He felt around to estimate the damage. No broken bones, apparently. The only wound he could find was a severe abrasion on his head. "Not so bad, after all," he surmised. "Struck his head on something and it knocked him out. Skull doesn't seem to be fractured. Doubt if there is much wrong with him, outside of spoiling his beauty, which was not great at any time." He straightened out the man's limbs, bathed his head, said some prayers.

In a few minutes the guide opened his eyes. As soon as he was conscious, he was all right. He felt about himself gingerly, asked what had happened, sat up. Nothing was the matter with him save for the throbbing cut in his scalp.

Xavier reassured him; told him he was all right, and not to worry. He would explain to the Ambassador. An accident might happen to anybody. It would be a job to climb up to the path again, but they could manage it, after he got rested. Besides, the soldiers would come along soon and, no doubt, could help. It was a much-chastened guide who listened to his charitable rescuer. Xavier waited until he had collected himself. As they sat on stones to wait, he opened a conversation.

"You know who sent you over this precipice?"

"The devil, I guess."

"Guess again. It was God. How long since you have been to confession?"

"Oh, Padre, don't ask me," groaned the guide. "Longer than I care to remember. I lead a rough life. I gave up all that long ago." The man buried his head in his hands.

"I thought you had strayed pretty far. Why else would you need such a severe lesson? God teaches people in whatever way they can learn. This is His grace coming to you, even though it took the peculiar form of a fall on your head." The man looked surprised. The novelty of this doctrine interested him. Xavier pressed the advantage.

"It means that He hasn't given you up. He wants to bring you back. After all, why aren't you dead? It's a miracle that you are not. An almighty hand guided you down here; it was the shock that saves. This is your chance." Xavier sent him his shafts like a fencer, but softened them by his gentle manner and charming smile. Grace, gratitude, and gentility gradually worked their will in the stubborn soul of the injured man. He sparred; Xavier comforted and coaxed. Suddenly it ended. The man threw himself on his knees to make the confession that would bring the prodigal son back to the circle of his Father's grace and love.

A word to the Ambassador put all right. "I owe you an apology," laughed Xavier in conclusion. "I thought you were too severe in scolding this man last night. But it was what he needed. He had to get worse before he got better. That's what sent him riding to a fall."

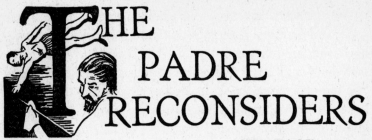THE PADRE RECONSIDERS

HIS FACE was set toward the East. The call had come to start out on the long march to that new world of teeming millions, exotic manners, and fabled wealth, suddenly become accessible to the adventurous spirits of freebooting Europe; and the young priest was ready.

To the Spanish and Portuguese of that day there was nothing strange in this; Catholic lands had Catholic viewpoints. That the priest should go for God where the soldiers and sailors were going for the flag, and the ragtag and bobtail for private gain, appeared the most natural thing in the world. Yet he was very young, this erstwhile Spanish nobleman in the shoddy soutane, and of a delicate mold and gentle manners that seemed to equip him oddly for the wild, rough life before him.

So thought the hearty old chaplain of Notre Dame of Nazareth in the city of Lisbon, as he regarded the guest who had come to spend the night with him, so that he might say Mass at that well-known shrine before leaving on his long journey. The King had given his final royal approval, and everything was arranged for the departure of the expedition on the morrow.

The young Spaniard was a picture of quiet modesty, as he responded to his host's queries. "No doubt it will be a

43

hard life, Father, but Almighty God can fit the back to the burden. I go with confidence in Him," he was saying to the solicitous old man.

"Yes, I dare say," replied the chaplain. "Yes, it's probably the best thing for you. You priests who go out there don't need much preparation, I suppose, do you? Nothing to do but teach catechism and try to get those roustabout soldiers to go to church once in a while. The work at home requires a lot more of a man. Have you exercised the ministry much anywhere?"

"Not much," replied the younger man. "Nothing to signify. I preached a bit in various towns in Italy. I was ordained only four years ago."

"Where did you make your studies?"

"At the University of Paris."

The chaplain's eyes widened a bit. "Well, you must have had a pretty good course," he commented. "How long were you there?"

"Nine years."

"Nine years! What were you doing there all that time?"

"After I got my degree, I taught Philosophy for several years."

"Indeed!" replied the now thoroughly surprised chaplain. "Indeed." And at a loss for further comment, he went to his snuffbox for inspiration. "What's this new Society you belong to? One would think there were enough of them in the Church already. Is it a missionary society? Are the requirements very strict?"

"We call it the Company of Jesus. The requirements are rather strict, although anyone can aspire to be a member; otherwise, I should never have got in. The idea is a specially

44

drilled army of religious to be on call for the needs of the Church. Our ambitions are largely missionary, but we are bound by a special vow to stand ready to engage in any work assigned us by the Holy Father. We are only a few men, and the Society is just beginning. You must pray, Father, that God will bless our little efforts."

"That I will, young man," replied the old chaplain heartily. By this time he had conceived a considerable respect and liking for his chance guest. The modest young priest more than measured up to the most exacting of standards. "May God bless you and your work. And now, let's go to bed. A good night's sleep won't hurt you before you start on your long trip. I've arranged for your Mass in the morning. You'll find everything prepared on the Blessed Virgin's altar. By the way, I shall be out on Communion calls for a couple of hours in the morning. Do please wait for me, and we can have breakfast together. If any call comes while I am out, will you take care of it for me? But it isn't likely; nothing much ever happens here. Well, good-night and God bless you."

The young missioner was finishing his Mass the next morning when he became conscious of a considerable commotion going on in the vacant field adjoining the church. A group of people were gesticulating and milling about. As he returned to the sacristy an excited individual rushed in. "Where is the pastor? Are you the only priest around? Please come quickly. There's a dying man out here."

"What's it all about?" returned the priest calmly. Meanwhile, however, he was doffing his vestments with remarkable expedition.

"A duel," replied the other. "We couldn't stop them.

They fought it out just now with swords, and young Silva got a thrust right through the body. He's a dying man. He is bleeding."

By this time they were out of the sacristy. Approaching the little knot of people, they found the fallen man lying on the ground in their midst, while one of his friends was trying—apparently without success—to staunch the flow of blood from his wound. His assailant stood apart with a few other men, in gloomy contemplation of the serious outcome of the encounter.

"He's dying, Padre," whispered a bystander, as the priest bent over the prostrate casualty.

"Well, if he is, let me have a word with him, good people," returned the priest. "Dying is a unique occasion in a man's life, and he ought to have a chance to do it right. Just withdraw a moment, won't you please, while I do what I can for his soul."

Left alone with the stricken man the priest found him perfectly conscious, and proceeded at once to exhort him to a good confession. All went well until the absolution. The penitent was not penitent at all, when it came to the question of pardoning his adversary. The priest tried everything; no amount of persuasion could move the obdurate man.

"I prefer to go to hell," he replied to the priest's final appeal to the justice of God. "I'd kill him now, if I could. I'll lose my soul before I'll pardon him."

The priest was baffled, but not for long. He suddenly had an idea. If this man is so insensible to the welfare of his soul, how about his body? He bent down and examined the wound. Then he straightened up and stood rapt for a moment, sending a swift arrow of prayer to God.

What did he see or learn from above, or below? That this was truly a superficial wound that entailed no grave danger, or that heaven would reward his prayer on the man's behalf? He gave no indication, but turned with smiling confidence to his penitent. "But will you pardon him, my child, if God accords you your life?"

"My life?" stammered the wounded man, suddenly eager. "What do you mean? But I can't get well, Father. They said I was dying. I feel it."

"I promise you God will restore your life, if you will only forgive. Come now, of course you will. Say you for-give."

"Well, Father, that's different, of course," came hesi-tatingly. The desire to live was strong. "Why, in that case, I suppose I might. Father, do you really mean it? Yes, I forgive — after all — it was as much my fault as his, anyhow. And, if I get well, I'll turn over a new leaf. I've been staying away from church too much. That's the whole trouble."

Breakfast was a simple affair, consisting of a biscuit and a glass of wine; and a half hour later the priest was sum-moned to it by the genial old chaplain, just returned from his Communion calls.

"I know all about it," was the first thing the chaplain said. "I was just leaving the hospital when they brought that young Silva in. He isn't going to die. The doctor says he is in no danger. The young imp told me you had already heard his confession, and that he is going to reform, and everything else. It's about time! I've been after that scape-grace for a long time. How in the world did you do it? Silva says you saved his life. Well, it's the first time I ever heard of a duel doing any good. I'd be willing to have some more of my people fight the idiotic things, if they all ended up that way."

"God can conquer evil with good," murmured the missionary. "Also, I learned a trifle of medicine at Paris, when I wasn't studying philosophy."

"Or saying your prayers, you young humbug," smiled the old man. "I heard what the people said. They thought he was going to die from that cut. Well, have it your own way. As for me, I have my opinion. And you'll pardon an old man, won't you, for what I said last night about exercising the ministry at home? It is plain to be seen that you would exercise it with the greatest success anywhere."

The venerable priest had not exaggerated, for the apostolic career to be fulfilled by his young guest was destined to make history. And with more words of generous praise and a parting blessing, the old pastor said good-bye to Francis Xavier, as the latter strolled lightly off to the carrack that was that day to bear him away from Europe forever.

SICK BAY

THE GOVERNOR was worried. It was not his first trip to the East, and he was accustomed to the decimations of the scurvy and the strange fevers that marked most passages. But this was an epidemic. Eighty men dead already. Possibly he had mismanaged a bit. Eight hundred men were too many to carry in this ship. The crowding was unmerciful.

Still, there was no traveling without all these sailors; and what was the use of going to Goa at all without the soldiers to reinforce the garrison? They might as well die on shipboard as get their throats cut after they landed. Who could have counted on being becalmed for forty days? And nothing but contrary winds when they did blow. Thank God they had made Mozambique anyhow. Not much of a place, but at least they were getting fresh food instead of that eternal cured meat.

"And thank God for those three Padres," he finally ruminated. "What we would do without them, I don't know. All the men would be dead by this time." A sudden idea came to him. He tapped a bell for the orderly.

"Ask Father Xavier to step in here a minute. You will find him in the sick bay, probably."

The orderly saluted and went out. "They say that Father Xavier is the sickest one of the lot," reflected the Governor. "If anything happens to him, we shall be in the soup.

49

I shall have to make him spare himself a bit."

A few minutes later, the Governor turned from his maps and papers to greet the young priest who entered smiling and calm. The Governor looked at him closely. The smile could not hide the flushed brow and glittering eyes of high fever. "Sit down, Padre," invited the Governor, and then turned to him with real solicitude.

"I am worried about you. They say you are the sickest man of the whole party. I can see for myself you are burning up with fever right this minute. Now look here, we don't want to lose you. You are doing wonderful work for the men. You are keeping up the morale. We couldn't get along without you. But, for Heaven's sake, go slow. Go to bed, man. Stop running around looking after all these soldiers and sailors, and give yourself a chance. The other Fathers can take care of them while you take a good rest."

Father Xavier laughed. "Glad you think I am doing some work, Excellency," he replied. "But actually the other Fathers are doing it all now. We have made a division of labor. The other Fathers are doing all the nursing, while I take care only of the spiritual work—trying to get the men to go to confession and all that."

"That may be," said the Governor, "but you are on your feet all the time, and you ought to be in bed."

Father Xavier grew serious. "Some of these poor fellows are pretty hard cases," he replied. "What am I going to do? Let them die in their sins? God is merciful, and I am His minister, thrown here by His Providence to give these poor fellows their last chance. I have a sailor on my hands now who has been raving for three days. He can't get well,

50

and I've got to watch him for a lucid moment. He needs it, too, poor chap. I was hobnobbing with him on the voyage and he has been a tough fellow, though good at heart. It's a rough life these men lead, and I shudder to think of any of them dying without confession."

The Governor sighed. A man of strong faith himself, he appreciated the reasoning of the young priest, and yet remained unconvinced. He did not see why Fathers Cam-erino and Mansilhas could not hear the confessions, in addi-tion to their other work, while the sick priest took a rest. What he did not realize was that the task was not merely to hear confessions, but rather to persuade hardened and despairing cases to go to confession. In this work Father Xavier was unique. Whether it was on account of the whole nights he spent kneeling on his cabin floor in prayer, or because of the communicative quality of a consuming faith, the fact was that few souls escaped him. Men who started out by blaspheming everything holy, and violently refusing his ministrations, would often end with a lamblike acceptance of them, after a few days' exposure to his patience and charity.

The Governor fidgeted around, drummed on his desk, looked sternly at the priest. "Now look here, Father Fran-cis," he finally said, "you are always preaching obedience to the rest of us. Why don't you give us a little example? I am going to have the doctor in here to look you over right now. Will you do what he says? Please try to be sensible. I am really very seriously worried about you."

Father Xavier considered a minute. "Why, yes," he said at length. "I am disposed to try to follow the doctor's advice. I'll go to bed if he orders me to, at least, for a time. Of course, I'll have to continue to keep a bit of an eye on the men. Better my body to die than their souls."

"Fine logic," broke in the Governor. "And you are the man who taught Philosophy at the University of Paris. If your body dies, we can say good-bye to their souls right there and then—the whole crowd of the troublesome rascals. Well, that sounds better anyhow. I'll get the doctor."

The doctor's examination was brief, and his verdict was that Father Xavier should have been in bed days ago. He prescribed immediate bleeding, in accordance with the medical practice in vogue at that time. The Governor was elated. The Father was ordered off to his cabin to be put to bed without ceremony. He consented after first going to take a look at his sailor. The poor man was still out of his senses. Then Father Francis was bundled into bed, the Governor looking on with satisfaction.

"Stay there now," he admonished on leaving. "I shall step around in the morning to see how you are getting on." The bleeding was administered, and the priest sank back exhausted. He fell into fitful slumber.

The next morning the Governor arrived at his desk in a pleased mood. The gentle monsoon breeze had played around all night, making possible the welcome change of a refreshing sleep. The mosquitoes had seemed not quite so voracious as usual. The steward had dug up a pleasant addition to breakfast in the shape of a luscious fruit the natives called papaya. As far as he knew, no further deaths had occurred. And the sick Padre was in bed! He chuckled as he recalled the persuasion he had had to use to get him there. "I can't blame him, in a way. Why not be all priest, if you are going to be a priest at all? But there's reason in everything. Anyhow, I got the best of him this time. He's in bed and that's something."

An idea suddenly energized him. "Might as well stroll around and see how he is, I suppose." He went to the cabin door, knocked gently. No answer. "Probably asleep," he surmised, pushing open the door. He looked at the bed. It was occupied, and by a sick man, but not by Francis Xavier. Stretched out in it lay the dying sailor; and kneeling on the bare floor in low conversation with him was the priest he had come to seek.

"So that's the way you go to bed—" sputtered the Governor. But the priest silenced him with a gesture.

"You can come in all right," he explained. "Kneel down here with me, and we'll say a few prayers. He's dying. It's all right, though. I've prepared him for a good death. It was hard work watching for a lucid moment. I could not see any other way to do but to put him in my bed, so I could keep an eye on him. Strangely enough, almost as soon as he got into it, he became calm and made his peace with God."

The Governor knelt down, and they recited several psalms and the Litany of the Blessed Virgin. The Governor arose. The dying man was breathing his last. Francis Xavier whispered ejaculations in his ear. The Governor went softly out.

Back in his office, the Governor sat musing. "Strange; he said it was strange. Well, it isn't strange to me, Father Francis. If I ever get sick, the first place I shall make for is your bed. I shan't undertake again to keep *you* in it, though," he ended with a chuckle.

He turned to his cares of state. "After all," he added as he began to sort over his papers, "I wonder if his particular brand of folly isn't what they call the folly of Christ."

THE MIXER

IN THE bright sun of a perfect Sunday morning a large congregation was streaming from the doors of the Cathedral. The variegated assembly included sprinklings from all classes of cosmopolitan Goa, ranging from the Governor with his staff to the latest converts among the pariah coolies. Almost the first person to come out, just as he had been pretty well the last one to go in, was Antonio Silva. Strangely enough, although Antonio had been too busy to arrive on time and could scarcely afford to wait until the service was over, he now suddenly found himself, once safely clear of the sacred edifice, with plenty of leisure. Time, a moment before so precious, immediately resumed its normal place in his life as something of very little consequence, after all.

To do him justice, there were extenuating reasons for his whilom regard for the value of time. On this particular morning he had sacrificed, if unwittingly and unwillingly, a little more time than usual to his devotions. He had not only given to God one whole half-hour out of the three hundred and thirty-six like periods contained in his week, but in addition he had been caught for an extra fifteen minutes by an unexpected sermon. Preaching at the late Mass was the exception rather than the rule; but the new priest, apparently in blissful ignorance of the convenient custom, had preached serenely away, despite the fidgeting of the Governor and the surprise of the whole congregation. "And what a sermon!" grumbled Antonio to himself. "It's easy to see that priest is new to the Far East. He must think we are all monks and nuns, with his talk about praying and going to the Sacraments all the time. I wish he lived in the world, like the rest of us. It's too bad these priests do not mix around a bit with the people. They would soon see the world isn't one big monastery."

Still, Antonio's little dissatisfaction was short-lived. The ordeal was over, and life resumed its normal aspect. Instead of husbanding time, his problem now magically reversed itself into a question of finding some way to waste it. He diminished his pace to a loiter, scanning the throng for a sight of some of his cronies with whom he might foregather. He did not have far to look. Most of the Portuguese in Goa knew each other, and were usually willing to admit it, for the class pretensions of the sixteenth century were not so powerful to keep them apart as was the common bond of exile to bring them together. Antonio soon bumped into a friend. It was De Sousa, a dealer in the pepper trade like himself, but a much older man; one of the most respected merchants of the town.

"Good, Antonio, glad to see you here," beamed the older man. "Haven't seen you at church for a long time. You young fellows don't come as often as you might, I'm afraid."

"Well, you know how it is in business, Senhor De Sousa," countered Antonio, not too pleased at this rather abrupt criticism but willing to accept it from the highly respected old man. "A man can't spend all his time in church."

De Sousa smiled, and Antonio felt that he had made rather a weak defense. It was indeed as weak as any defense might well be, as nobody in the wildest flight of fancy could ever have accused Antonio of spending all his time in church. His grievance came back to him, and he clutched at the means of bolstering his position. "Of course, I know I might come more often. But look how it is. Here's this morning, for instance. When a man does take the time from his business to come, you run into a long service with a lot of preaching and all that."

"Didn't you like the sermon?" asked the old merchant.

"No, I did not," replied Antonio bluntly. "First of all, we ought not to have any sermon at all at the late Mass. It's not the custom. And of all the sermons! What's the use to tell us all to live like a lot of priests and Sisters? Is there any sense in that?"

"I'm not so sure that there is not a lot of sense in it, Antonio. Why let the priests and Sisters monopolize all the good things? Is religion only for them?"

"No, only it's different. The Lord doesn't expect as much from us merchants. And if that new priest had any sense, he would know it."

"Well, it's true that circumstances alter cases," soothed the old man, not relishing an argument that early in the day. "And we can all save our souls in different ways, if we do our part. By the way, have you met the new priest?"

"No," replied Antonio, surprised. "Why should I meet him? I don't want to meet him."

"He's a most amazing man," pursued De Sousa. "Lives in the hospital caring for the sick, and is all over the town besides, preaching, teaching, doing everything. Most charming fellow, too. You couldn't help liking him."

Antonio was just about to declare roundly that he felt

56

entirely capable of not liking the new priest, when that individual suddenly appeared. The crowd was thinning out, and the priest was just parting from a lingering group of children, when his eye strayed to De Sousa. He strolled over for a word with the old man.

"I was just telling Senhor Silva about you, Father," said De Sousa with a malicious twinkle, "and I'm glad you came along. Father Xavier, this is Antonio Silva. He's in the pepper trade, the same as I am."

Antonio shook hands, looked at the ground, mumbled something. Father Xavier began some noncommittal talk. At first Antonio said nothing. De Sousa kept the conversation going. But the priest directed an occasional remark at Antonio, and he was obliged to answer. The priest was gracious, witty and always smiling. Antonio went unconsciously from silence to monosyllables, to grudging smiles, to awakened interest, finally to whole-souled conversation. The man he had regarded as needing to mix with people was giving him a first-class demonstration of that very art. Xavier kept on until he saw that his new acquaintance was fairly well thawed. When he quitted the pair to go back to his residence at the hospital, he left two friends instead of one.

Antonio and Xavier met fairly often after that. The priest had a way of stopping for a moment whenever he saw a crowd, and the busy Antonio usually found time to make one of the idle group that gathered mornings on the quay whenever there was any unusual news, and evenings in the square when there wasn't. Xavier gave only a word and a smile here and there, and was gone, but it took only a few of these encounters to make Antonio forget his remnant of reserve. Twice Xavier stepped into his shop for a brief word about nothing in particular. Antonio gave his friendship. "That priest likes me for some reason," was his unconscious thought. And thereupon he proceeded to like the priest.

When people all over Goa began to invite the missionary to their houses, and it was known that he was not averse to an occasional visit, Antonio began to be a little proud of his acquaintanceship with the popular new priest. "Suppose I ought to invite him to my place," he mused. "Everybody else does. And some of them don't know him half as well as I do," he reflected with flattered satisfaction. He hesitated as another thought intruded. "Wonder if he would start lecturing me? Doesn't seem that kind. And he knows how everybody lives here, anyhow. I'm no worse than the rest." He put the thought away, comforted. "Think I'll ask him," he concluded briskly. "He's not like the rest of these priests who know nothing about the world." He recalled vaguely that he had expressed the exactly opposite opinion about the same man only a few days before. "I quite misjudged him at first," he admitted generously.

He started angling for an opportunity to invite Xavier, without realizing that a better angler than himself had the very same object in view. The chance soon came. He stopped Father Xavier on the way to the hospital, and was gratified when the busy priest promptly accepted his invitation without the least demur. In fact, he seemed distinctly pleased, even eager. "Fine fellow," thought Antonio. "No fuss about it. Acts like a human being. Why, he is glad to come."

Antonio Silva was a man who had his own talents, only

they did not shine very brightly in his religious life, because he chose to consecrate them exclusively to his life work of trading in pepper. He was a keen merchant. Money came easily. He lived in luxury. Xavier found his house an ornate affair. Inside it was filled with soft rugs, silk draperies, tumbling children, and innumerable servants. Xavier greeted the youngsters, told his host a joke, and they sat down to dinner. A servant stood behind each chair wielding a peacock-feather fan, while others glided in and out with the dishes and wines. Antonio beamed. He was a good entertainer, and he dutifully began the cheerful chatter that hosts affect.

But his efforts to season his banquet with the spice of wit did not proceed very far. Father Xavier was only toying with the first course, as most of his attention was going to the children. He seemed fascinated by them, watching them, smiling at them. Also, he kept looking around as if something were amiss. He was listening to Antonio with half an ear, and then suddenly he missed a remark altogether. Or at least he appeared to do so. "Oh, pardon me, Senhor Silva," he interjected. "I'm afraid I did not quite follow you. Such lovely children. They distracted me. I can hardly take my eyes off them."

"Oh, the children. Good of you to say so. Yes, they are good children," replied Antonio in a little wonderment. Xavier had expressed this same sentiment about the children when he first came in, and there did not seem to be any particular occasion for harping on it.

"Too bad they have lost their mother so young. It must be a great anxiety to you to care for them alone," purred Xavier consolingly.

59

Antonio looked up sharply, as he began to see which way the wind was blowing. But he scented the trouble too late. He was in for it now. Try to beat around the bush? He glanced at the clear-eyed young missioner and gave up the notion at once. No use trying to pull the wool over the eyes of a man like that. He shifted in his chair uneasily a moment, and then took the plunge. "Their mother is not dead, Father," he muttered. "She is right here in the house. Maybe I should have brought her to see you, but you know how it is in these countries. We fall into the Oriental customs, and the women don't mix with other people. Besides she knows only a few words of Portuguese anyhow." Antonio paused, unexpectedly pleased with his effort. Under the spur of his difficulty he felt he had managed to invent a fairly good defense after all.

Xavier decided it was time to be very direct. "Tell her to come in," he said. The attack was delivered with offhand geniality. "Surely you want to introduce me to your wife, and for my part I am anxious to meet her. You see, I shan't be able to come often, as I am so busy. And we are such good friends that I want to know all your family."

That ended the short struggle. Antonio excused himself. A few moments later he returned, escorting a prepossessing young Indian woman. She looked scared, but she bowed to Father Xavier and sank into a chair. Xavier was graciousness itself. He set himself to put the newcomer at her ease in her own house, and between his praise of the children and his gentle overtures in the simplest of Portuguese, he soon succeeded. The conversation was general, if a bit halting. The dinner went along smoothly. Antonio was surprised to find things going so pleasantly, and almost regretted that he had not included his helpmate from the beginning. Yet he knew in his heart that a reckoning was coming.

Like most busy priests, Xavier's habit was to eat and run. He stayed just long enough after the meal to speak a few confidential words to Antonio. "Fine woman," he said. "You are fortunate to have such a good mother for your children. Now when shall we supply the little omission? Let us say tomorrow morning at the Cathedral rectory. I'll speak to the pastor. What time can you bring her over?"

Antonio gasped, sputtered, put forth his last feeble effort. "Look here, Father, you don't know life in the Orient, I'm afraid. It's different around here. I'm not the only one who isn't married. It's the custom. You see, if I go back to Portugal later on . . ."

Father Xavier cut him off. "Portugal is a Christian country. You know what the custom is there. If you go back, go back right. You also know what the custom is in the Church. There are a few customs for you, if that's what you want." His victim was looking at the floor. He patted him on the back and sent home a clincher. "What is the use to be friends, if you won't let me help you, Antonio? There is a fine woman whom you are not treating properly. You could not have a better wife. And there's your own soul. Are you treating it right? Don't expect me to be satisfied until I get you straightened out. What kind of friendship would that be?"

Antonio gave up. He knew a lost battle when he saw it. And he also had a sudden happy feeling that in losing this contest he had surprisingly won. Somehow a strange peace was now invading his soul, and it was all the more

61

welcome because long unaccustomed. He even felt a sudden rush of gratitude towards this unusual friend, who recalled him so irresistibly to his better self. For he had one; not dead but buried, and in spite of himself, he welcomed its resurrection. "Thanks, Father," he said simply. "We'll be there."

His pious entreaty had been granted. The man who wanted to see the clergy mix more with the people and get acquainted with the world had seen his wish come true. He had met a mixer.

MANUEL

HEAD-OVER-HEELS

THE DOOR of his nipa hut swung gently open. The aperture disclosed a pair of very bright eyes that beamed from a diminutive brown form. He had a visitor. No, a lot of visitors, for the first dusky midget that sidled in was followed by a file of companions, and Father Xavier suddenly found himself host to a dozen young Parava boys. He jumped up, smiling and pantomiming a welcome he did not entirely feel. Here was just a little practical application of his general problem. "Scarcely knowing a word of the language," he thought, "I shall have a hard time even to entertain these youngsters."

But this fear proved unfounded, for he had reckoned without his guests. Their own curiosity kept them fully entertained, so that there was no need for extra effort on the part of the host. Everything about the hut and its inmate seemed to interest them, and for a space they twittered about like a flock of magpies in a harvest field. After a thorough appraisal of everything, they gradually settled down to concentrate on the smiling face and the few stammered words of their new-found friend.

The Father thanked his stars that before leaving Goa he had had the foresight to draw up and commit to memory a statement of the most important truths of religion, to gether with the principal prayers, in the Tamil language. He tried them on his boyish audience. Sallies of laughter greeted his pronunciations. He joined in the mirth. The boys were immediately interested, and soon a little class was in progress, with both professor and pupils teaching and learning.

It was an hour later when Xavier finally picked up his breviary, and shooed out a lot of visitors who were loath to depart. The little chap who had first entered was the last to leave. He had something on his mind apparently. Father Xavier tried patiently to make out what it was, and after several wrong guesses he finally got a glimmer of light. "You want to know if you can come back tomorrow? Why, certainly. All of you." He opened his arms wide to include them all, and smiled a reassuring welcome.

It was not strange that Father Francis found it hard to understand in this particular case, for his little friend was not much given to intelligible speech in any language. His communications consisted chiefly of gestures, sometimes reinforced by monosyllables. Now he made no reply to the welcome invitation, but suddenly proceeded to turn cartwheels around the room. Xavier stared in amazement at this unconventional expression of gratitude. When the youngster had indicated his pleasure sufficiently by a final handspring, he flashed a good-bye smile, and vanished after the rest.

This proved to be the beginning of a novel catechist school. The boys found their new acquaintance a greater attraction than their usual pastimes of herding water buffaloes and gathering clams, and daily sessions in the missioner's hut soon became their set program. Other boys from nearby villages swelled the numbers. The first thing Xavier did was to resurrect their Christian names from the vague memories of parents and uncles and aunts, aided when necessary by the baptismal registers. The little acrobat turned out to be named Manuel, and he at once became very proud of his new appellation. In fact, he turned a handspring when it was disclosed to him, and immediately added several sentences to his limited vocabulary. "My name is Manuel," he would say on the slightest provocation. He persuaded the Father to write it on a slip of paper for him, and then proceeded to show it to all and sundry. "You see this?" he said to any body who would listen to him. "That's my name. Manuel." Then he would indulge in a cartwheel or two, and run off to pester the next comer.

The boys had good memories and they quickly learned much more than their own names. It was not very long before they knew everything that Xavier was able to teach them, and by this time the Father himself had also learned a few things that they were unconsciously teaching him. He found out that the children wielded a peculiar influence, due to the magic circumstance that they were now supposed to be studying books under his tutelage. In this primitive civilization, learning was esteemed in direct proportion to its scarcity, and as it was totally absent in any shape or form, its value was rated very high indeed. His boys were already looked upon as the scholars of the community. Actually, they were the nearest thing to it in those villages where no body had ever attended school for a single day of his life.

"We are glad the boys are learning books," one of the head men told Xavier. "We old men have no time, but our children will be scholars and all the villages will prosper."

The boys did not hide their newly acquired learning under a bushel, but took it home with them and began to preach it from the housetops. Soon every hut was resounding with the prayers and catechism lessons that the retentive little memories stored up and the facile little tongues loved to sing out. The mothers and fathers and brothers and cousins began to find the phrases on their own tongues from the force of constant hearing. Father Francis had unwittingly enlisted a small army of catechists who were performing, at no salary and in the greatest glee, a very creditable job of mass instruction.

When he called the boys his catechists, they were delighted; and for Manuel especially the high-sounding title was a new source of overweening pride. "I am a catechist," he went around shouting. When somebody asked him what that was, he puckered his brow and did some thinking. "I don't know," he finally admitted. "But I know I'm one, because Father Francis said I was."

Manuel, as a matter of fact, had every right to this title, for he proved to be one of the most zealous of these little instructors. He found his tongue now that ready-made words were given it to say, and nobody's voice was louder or more tireless than his in the incessant repetition of the catechism. Whoever came in any considerable contact with him was bound to learn unless he was deaf. Manuel indeed had almost too much zeal. At least, he had more of it than could be satisfied even by this engrossing work, and it was not long before he found an additional outlet for it. And that is how he got into trouble.

Father Francis was saying his breviary under the palms. Suddenly a very scared little Manuel appeared from nowhere, all out of breath. He did not turn a cartwheel this time, but saved his energy to cling to the Father's black gown. Before there was time to find out the trouble, the obvious cause of it appeared in the form of an irate villager, unmistakably seeking somebody to devour. Manuel clung closer.

Xavier watched the man approach, and in a moment the man looked up and saw him. He suddenly underwent a transformation. His ire cooled magically. In fact, it apparently vanished altogether, for his gesticulating rush now became a slow and unconcerned saunter. He pretended to be looking for some object on the ground. Now he was on the point of passing them by.

The priest smiled. He saw more in this than met the eye. "Come over here and tell me what is the trouble," he sang out.

This hearty invitation seemed to add greatly to Manuel's distress. He clutched the gown again. "Don't call him, Father," he whispered. "He is angry at me."

"Angry at you? Nonsense. What did you do to him?"

Manuel was saved the necessity of answering. The excited villager was nearer, and by the time he got close to the squirming Manuel, he momentarily forgot his awe of Father Xavier. "You little rascal," he burst out. "Coming into people's houses and breaking up their furniture. If the Father weren't here —"

"Wait a minute," interposed Father Xavier gently. "Evidently you've been having trouble. Both of you. But before making any more, let's find out what it is all about." He turned a mild gaze on the man. "Was Manuel bothering you?"

"He rushes into my house without a word to anybody, and begins throwing my things around. Breaking up my furniture and everything! Fine way of acting!" He became emboldened by the vehemence of his own eloquence. "I thought you were teaching these boys. If that is the kind of teaching —"

But this was too much for Manuel, and he promptly forgot his fears. Criticism of his teacher was where he drew the line. "Father is teaching us good things," he shouted, leaving the priest's side and hunching forward to emphasize his arguments by bendings and jumpings and contortions. "You don't need to say anything about the Father. Just tell him what kind of furniture I took. Just tell him once. I dare you."

Xavier began to see light. In these nipa huts there was not much furniture of any kind, in all conscience. The household goods of these homes were simple in the extreme. But in some of them there still lurked a few objects that did not belong there. "What kind of furniture was it?" he asked the man.

"It makes no difference what kind it was. He has no business coming into my house and —"

"It was his idols! That's what it was! His idols!" Manuel was shouting his best. "What do I want with his old furniture? All I did was to take his idols and throw them in the river." He turned anxiously to Father Francis. "Was it wrong, Father? I thought you said the idols were no good."

"I did not tell you to throw them in the river, Manuel," said Xavier mildly. "Though I confess it is not a bad place for them." He turned sternly to the crestfallen villager.

"But what have you to say? A Christian keeping idols in his house! Are you not ashamed? Why, the boy has really done you a favor." He paused for breath.

But the argument was already over. The man became suddenly interested in tracing patterns on the dusty path with his bare toe. "I was going to take them out myself, Father," he muttered.

Father Francis changed his tone immediately. "Of course, you were," he said kindly. "I know none of our Christians want idols in their houses." He smiled reassuringly.

This had a magic effect. The culprit regained his equanimity at once and with it his native wit for extemporaneous invention. He brightened, switched to a mood of expansive confidence. "You know me, Father, I am a Christian. You think I would have idols in my house? Certainly not. But you know how it is with these women folks. It was all on account of my half brother's mother-in-law. That old dame is the one who wanted to keep them. Of course, we men don't believe in such foolishness. I was just waiting for a good chance —"

"All right, all right," interrupted the priest. "The affair is well settled. The idols are out, and I will come after a while to bless your house and ask God to protect you. And don't molest Manuel. He was only trying to do you a favor." He turned to the boy. "And as for you, Manuel, you had better leave the idols to me in the future. I'll take care of them. I don't want a catechist who goes around mixing up in other people's business."

Manuel's heart suddenly did a somersault. He was just congratulating himself on being well out of a ticklish business, but the last dread sentence from Xavier's lips plunged

him again into the depths. He saw his precious title vanish-
ing. "Father," he cried, "can't I be a catechist any more? I
can still be a catechist, can't I? If I do what you tell me?"

The missionary paused, smiled, enjoyed the situation.
"Well, it's all right this time, Manuel," he said slowly.
"We'll let you be a catechist." He stooped and patted the
little head. "Yes, Manuel," he beamed, "I really want you
very much to be my catechist."

Manuel turned a double handspring. He was still describ-
ing cartwheels and other contortions all over the place, as
the priest turned to his breviary. "Out of the mouths of
babes and sucklings Thou hast perfected praise," mused
Francis Xavier, giving thanks where it was due, and greatly
marveling at the power of God to accomplish His work with
the most unexpected of means.

SILVERY MOON

A SOFT radiance filtered through the interlocked branches and spangled the jungle path with patches of silver. Francis Xavier realized gratefully, as he trudged along, that his visit to the most remote village of the Paravas was fortunately coinciding with the time of the full moon. It made a difference. Often the darkness caught him hunting his way along the forest paths, with little to guide him save the confidence that every path led to some village sometime. Frequently these late sorties, timed to find the people in their evening leisure, were punctuated with the falls and sprawlings and scratchings and tearings that the jungle exacts of unwary travelers. This evening, however, the walk was decidedly pleasant. The fatigue of the hot day was over, and he was fortified by his own sparing little bowl of rice and salt fish.

He wanted particularly to visit this village. Like all the Christian villages of the pearl fishers, it had not seen a priest for ten years; not since its people had been baptized with scant instruction on the original visit of Father Vaz. It was high time for another priest to call. "In fact," mused Xavier, as he sauntered along, "if the other villages are any criterion, this one probably needs me most of all." It was the most isolated, and for that reason would be the least Christian. Left without a priest, the villages that lay close together had at least a certain mutual association that

71

helped to remind them of their new Faith, but the distant villages had not even that tenuous bond to hold them. Worst of all, the greater the isolation, the less the protection.

When he finally stumbled on the village, he did not at once gain admission. Although he could see the lights through the trees, his repeated shouts brought no welcoming answer. He pressed up to the rude stockade and set an army of dogs to clamorous barking. By the time three excited men, all grasping savage-looking bolos, came out to meet him, he was beginning to feel uneasy. The moonlight again stood him in good stead. The truculent anxiety of the reception committee immediately turned to childlike pleasure.

"Oh, it's the Father," they shouted happily, much to Xavier's relief, and equally to their own. "It's the Father," re-echoed the cry from one end of the village to the other, as the gates were thrown open. People came running pell-mell. Children danced out, falling and tripping over each other; mothers grabbed up their babies and scrambled forward; the elders bustled forth in dignified haste. Xavier was kept busy trying to give a word or a nod to all, as they pressed around him.

But the hospitality of simple people is always thoughtful. "The Father is tired after his long walk," said one of the old men. "The Father is tired," repeated everybody. Soon Xavier found himself seated in the best matshed the village afforded, trying to refuse the food and drink that were pressed upon him, and finally compromising on a thimblelike cup of tea. He was glad to relax his tired muscles and settle back to a cheery evening of pleasant talk with his little flock.

72

"What an enjoyable walk I had," said Xavier, after he had finished his tea and smiled at everybody. "In the moonlight it is so easy to walk through the forest. Surely God is good to give us this beautiful moon to light our way."

This remark did not bring the hearty response that usually followed his smiling sallies. There was a slight hush. Gravely one old man replied, "Once we are liking the moonlight also, Father. But not any more."

Francis was surprised. Scenting some superstition, he went, as he thought, right to the point. "The moon is nothing to worry about, my children. Nothing but a lamp that God hung in the sky to be of service to us. You must not think there is anything lucky or unlucky about the moon."

"Well, it isn't that meaning exactly, Father," replied the old man a bit uneasily. "It is true we used to think a lot depended on the moon, but that was before we became Christians. You see, the trouble is this way. Suppose the moon lighting you through the forest is lighting other people also?" The old man paused; shook his head gloomily. A murmur of assent ran through the crowd. Evidently the old man was one of the Elders of the village. His word carried weight.

Xavier was still puzzled. "Who would come at this time of night?" he pursued. "All have eaten rice, and are preparing to go to sleep."

"That we are surely hoping," returned the spokesman for the crowd. "But it is also not certain. I am explaining to the Father. It's the Badagas!"

That magic word explained everything. The name of this marauding band of Mohammedan tribesmen had spread terror over the whole fishery coast. Time and again they descended on helpless villages in raids that included stealing, burning, capturing for ransom, and even at times wholesale massacre. Since the Paravas became Christians they had been harried by them more than ever. And the single little Portuguese fort on the coast that represented the only police power in that isolated region was unable, even when willing, to protect the scattered Christian villages from their depredations. Xavier was aware of this constant menace to his neophytes, and he had already protested to the Governor at Goa about the lack of adequate protection. He did not know that the Badagas were operating in the vicinity of this particular section at the moment. He surmised that the anxiety of the village was part of the general contagion of fear.

"What makes you worry about the Badagas? God will protect you. They are not in this locality at present, are they? And what has the moonlight to do with them, anyhow?"

The old Elder looked up. "That's just it, Father. They are in this locality right now. The rumor is coming that they raided a village only ten leagues away the night before last. Tonight is the full moon, and that's why we are afraid. The Badagas live over the mountains, and so they are strange to our forest. They do not know the paths, and that is why they pick out moonlight nights for their attacks."

The old man paused to emit a deep sigh in which the entire gathering straightway joined. Then he suddenly brightened, looked at the priest, and made an expansive gesture to indicate he had something important to add. "Believe me, we are always rejoicing to see the Father, but tonight most of all. We know the Badagas are not coming

74

when the Father is here. The Father is protecting us!"

"They are not coming when the Father is here," went up the chorus. "The Father is protecting us!" The cries were suddenly carefree, even joyous. It was so easy to shift the responsibility. Xavier suddenly felt that the shoe was now on the other foot. His desire to comfort his people had been replaced by a fear that he had succeeded too well. Their confidence in him was touching, but suppose the raiders did come? Well, there was God.

"I am not sure that I have any means to protect you, my children," he finally replied. "But God has. With Him to care for you, you are as safe here as in a fort. Don't worry. God will protect you."

He looked around and saw approval on every side. "God will protect us," echoed through the room.

That served as a good introduction to the catechism lesson. Father Xavier began with a little examination that soon revealed the presence of some novel theology in the heads of many, and the absence of any at all in the heads of most. One of the chief Elders was under the impression that the twelve apostles created heaven and earth. Somebody maintained that there were four Sacraments and seven marks of the Church. Many similar misapprehensions were aired. The great majority frankly admitted that they remembered nothing at all except the fact that they were Christians. Xavier was patient, and he forgot his fatigue in correcting and explaining and encouraging. The time flew by. After two hours of the unaccustomed mental exercise, however, the yawns became general, and Father Xavier also realized he was tired as he said good-night. He still had long prayers to say. Finally he lay down on his board for a little sleep.

Two o'clock in the morning is said to be the time when the courage and the general spirits of the ordinary man are at their very lowest ebb. Francis Xavier was an ordinary man, but he had an extraordinary confidence in God; and when he awoke at this unearthly hour to the sound of shouting and running and banging of doors, his sensations were those of mild curiosity. To him night alarms were a commonplace of mission life, anyhow. He still felt quite tired, but he said a prayer and promptly forgot it. He had dashed some water over his face and was picking up his crucifix, when the door suddenly burst open.

"Excuse me, Father. Oh, you are up already. Good!" It was the head Elder in great excitement; his palsied old hands were trembling twice as much as usual, and his voice quavered. Yet there was relief in his voice and manner also when he saw that the missioner was up and ready for business. He came close to Xavier's ear. "The Badagas are coming," he whispered, as if they were already in the room and might overhear him.

Xavier patted his visitor on the back and laughed out loud. It was as if the old man had announced that breakfast was ready. "Are they coming?" he bantered. "Well, so am I. That is, if you will give me time to wash my face. Only please rest your heart. Why get excited at this time in the morning?"

The missioner's calmness steadied the old man, but he was still unable to perceive any joke in the situation. "This is no time for laughing words, Father," he blurted out reproachfully. "Please hurry up. We men are all trying to decide

76

what to do. They are here, I tell you! A runner just came from the next village, and he says they will be here any minute. They are all riding horses. Hurry up!"

The missioner was losing no time, and with the end of this speech they were both out of the door. The clear moonlight shone down on a stockade full of people milling about in extraordinary confusion. Men were running here and there and shouting directions to each other to which nobody paid the least attention. Some were stringing arrows on bows; others were feverishly trying to barricade flimsy straw doors; a few big boys were lugging improvised ammunition consisting of stones and broken earthenware pots to a central pile. Women were rushing about, grabbing up babies, screaming and chattering. The children were having the best time of the lot. Not quite realizing what the pandemonium was about, they had no conscious thought except to add to it to the extent of their powers, and this they did by charging around helter-skelter and yelling with all their might. The only persons who appeared to have retained the use of their senses were the older men. They were grouped in front of the main gate to the village enclosure in anxious council. Xavier made straight for them, and immediately took charge of the whole performance.

"Stop all this fussing!" rang out his sharp command. "Line these people up, and let them listen to me." He put a little indignation into his tone. "Such carrying on! Am I not here to protect you? Hurry up now. Tell everybody to keep quiet. I am going to speak."

The mere sight of Xavier acted like magic, and the word spread around straightway calmed the hubbub. As soon as the missioner saw he could be heard, he launched out.

77

"My children," he began reproachfully, "there is no occasion to get excited. The Badagas are coming. All right. But you forget that God is always here to protect you. Does He not hold you in the hollow of His hand? And the Badagas also? Nothing can happen without His holy will. Now listen. You remain here quietly. Do whatever the chief Elder tells you. He is the head man. You can get your bows and arrows and line up here under his command. But stay inside the stockade and wait." He paused a moment to let this sink in. "Now then," he continued briskly. "Where are these Badagas? I am going out to meet them."

"But, Father, you can't go," expostulated one of the Elders. That gave rise to a soaring chorus of interruptions. "The Father is getting killed," wailed one. "The Badagas don't know who he is," suggested another. "He does not even know their language, so how is he talking to them?" objected a third. "Stay with us, Father," shrieked some. "Don't let the Father go," implored others.

Xavier did not listen to their objections. His voice cut through the din again. "Does anybody here know the Badaga language?"

"No, Father," replied a volunteer. "They live many miles to the north over the mountains. We are not mixing with them. No, nobody knows a word of their language."

"Then I go alone."

A hush fell on the crowd. Something about the simple sentence transcended the moment, and anxious hearts forgot their own frantic fears for a space in the abrupt disclosure of a heart that knew no fear.

Another instant, and the cries and shouts of objection arose again in a wailing crescendo. "They are killing him," moaned the women, with their genius for sympathy. "Yes, they are killing the Father, and after that they are killing us," chorused the men, with their genius for pessimism. The uproar swelled again, as if to make up for lost time.

Xavier was once more calm and smiling, and that meant he was going into action. He did not need to ask the way a second time, for suddenly the sound came of men crashing through the jungle. "The main path," he thought. "I shall just have time to meet them in the clearing. Good there's a moon." He was at the gate.

"Keep a good watch," he said to the Elder on guard. He looked closer and recognized the same old patriarch who had come to awaken him. "Let nobody follow me out," he said to the old man. "This is my job." He held up his crucifix and turned for a last word. "Say some prayers, my children. I will come right back. God bless you." He was gone.

Everybody obeyed his orders except the old man to whom he had committed them. The trembling old Elder watched the missioner skim along the moonlit path, as he began reluctantly to close the gate. Suddenly he forgot his fears. "I am going with him," he heard himself muttering, rather to his own surprise. "If he is getting killed, I am dying with him." On the impulse of the moment he slipped out the gate, shut it behind him, and was off down the path after the speeding blackrobe.

The clearing was only a few hundred yards away. The old Elder paused at the edge of it, and looked cautiously out from the trees that fringed and concealed the end of the village path. A gorgeous full moon was shining down on a bizarre sight. Drawn up in massed ranks at the opposite end of the plain stood an army of strange-looking men.

There were hundreds of them. All were armed, some with long spears and fantastic shields, others with bows and arrows.

Fronting them was a thin and worn-looking figure in a long black gown. One upraised arm held the crucifix. With the other he was gesticulating vigorously. And he was shouting in some language that the old Elder had never heard. Neither had the Badagas, apparently, to judge from their nonplussed attitude. But what was that outlandish figure that seemed to sprawl across half the field? It was waving and weaving about just like Xavier. Why, it was Xavier, of course, or rather his reflection. The moonlight was flooding over his shoulder at a peculiar angle that cast a fantastic shadow, thirty feet high, athwart the clearing.

What was happening now? The old Elder could not make it out. An uneasiness seemed to spread through the Badagas. There were sudden howls here and there; a few were falling on their knees, raising hands to heaven. Suddenly someone barked an order. The front rank broke for the road at the other end of the plain. The howls and shouts became general. Now the whole army was retreating in a confused jumble. Cries and imprecations resounded, as they ran down the road and crashed through the bush. The old Elder could scarcely believe his eyes. Xavier was alone in the moonlight.

"How did it happen?" said Francis later, when he had returned to the village and quieted the fears of his flock. "Why, to tell the truth, I do not know myself. I spoke Goanese to them, and there might have been somebody in the crowd who understood it. Although I doubt it, since nobody answered me. Then there was my strange appearance, for they probably never saw a priest before. We must thank God, my children, for His good moonlight that enabled our friends to see me. And likewise that shadow of mine! Really it almost scared me when I first saw it. Extraordinary! And don't forget the Cross. They did not understand me, no doubt, but the Cross speaks a language of its own." He beamed on them all, as they drank in his words. "But after all, you know, it does not really matter what happened. The main thing is that God protected you, for He can choose any means He likes. Now doesn't He take good care of His own? And are you not glad that you trusted in Him?"

"Yes, Father," came the fervent chorus. "And thank you, Father, for protecting us," somebody added in a jubilant shout.

"No!" insisted Xavier. "You must not thank me. It is God who is protecting you. You must thank God."

"Yes, Father," concluded the old Elder simply. "We thank God. We know He is protecting us. That is the reason He sent you to us tonight."

UP a TREE

"I WOULDN'T visit that village, if I were you, Father Francis." John Vaz looked worried — which was not a usual condition with him, for his years of knocking about in India had made him more or less ready for anything. "You will never reach Travancore at all, if you don't use a little caution. Remember, we are getting away from the Coast now and these people are different." The young Portuguese trader had risen from the low stool he was squatting on, to stretch his legs. He took a few steps and turned abruptly to face his companion again. "Maybe you don't realize how serious this is, Father," he said. "There is real danger, I tell you."

"Do you really think so, John?" Father Francis was smiling. "It's good of you to be so solicitous about me. But nothing has happened yet."

"Father! you don't know these people!" The young man stopped his striding again. "There was a lot of talk when you stopped to preach in those last two villages. That always stirs up the Brahmins, you know. That old man in Three Bamboos told me they were going to make trouble if they got a chance. They can easily do it, you know. They only need to say a word to some gang of local rowdies and they would kill you without a thought. Nobody would ever know the difference. Where would you get any protection around here?"

82

"Protection? Wait a minute, my son." Father Francis was roused. "We get protection from God — here and everywhere else. Don't worry about that part. Now listen. I've got to visit that village. I was fortunate to get the invitation. The village people are friendly and want me to come — and all the Brahmins in India won't stop me. But don't worry. We shall soon get to Travancore and see the Rajah and then it will be better. The only thing is that I cannot refuse now — or any time — to explain the Faith to friendly people because some Brahmin does not like it. Is that clear?"

John Vaz shrugged his shoulders and gave up. "I knew you were going to say that, Father," he said. "All right," he added resignedly. "I only hope nothing happens to you. When will you be back?"

"They will probably expect me to spend the night with them, but it's not certain," the missioner answered. "I ought to get there about suppertime when they are in from the fields. If there is no place to stay, though, I will come back tonight."

"Well, that's it, you see," said the missioner's friend. "I don't like traveling around at night in a place like this. Not after the warning that old man gave us. It's so easy for anything to happen." The young trader was just taking a parting shot. He knew when Father Xavier had made up his mind. He turned away and began to plan how to spend the day until his companion returned — and to wonder what to do if he did not return.

If Father Francis had stood still long enough, he could have passed for a scarecrow. He had given up his tattered cassock and worn-out shoes for the loose-fitting, native loba and a pair of straw sandals. His bearded face was pale and haggard from his weeks of scanty food and constant travel. His tall, wiry frame was thin to angularity. A cheap umbrella held over his head completed the outline of the gaunt figure that went flapping along the path through the paddy fields. Occasionally the path left the cultivated land and wandered through a patch of scrub forest where the shade was refreshing. But mostly he was in the open under the hot sun. He strode along as if in haste. Nobody else in all that torpid land was in a hurry, but he still retained the habit of energy that was the birthright of his Basque mountains. And he bore a message that could not wait.

The visit was all he could desire. The village people were genuinely glad to see him. The head Elders welcomed him with every mark of respect, and the little boys and girls came promptly sidling around him in their innocent genius for making friends. He was not there ten minutes before the whole village became a big family-gathering with himself in the middle of it. The people knew something about the Church and wanted to know more. They had acquaintances in another village who had become Christians. One old man had even been all the way to the Pearl Fishery Coast where he had seen whole districts giving adhesion to the Church. Father Francis talked and joked with them for two hours. He kept up a constant chatter while eating supper with the men. All the time he took pains to explain the truths of religion carefully and forcefully in his mixture of the grave and gay. They were interested and he was happy. They made him promise to put their village on his list for further visits when he or his missioners came into their district to stay.

It was getting late and the missioner began to wonder if

84

his hosts expected him to spend the night with them. He talked on, but the conversation began to lag and still nobody came forward with an invitation. Suddenly he sensed that some of the old men seemed uneasy about something. They fidgeted a little and appeared distracted. The missioner watched them. "They probably have no place in this poor little village to give me," he thought. He jumped up to go through his leave-taking.

The old men hobbled forward and beckoned to him. They wanted some private conversation. The oldest patriarch of the lot was the spokesman. He put his mouth close up to the missioner's ear. "Father staying, trouble coming," he quavered. "We feel ashamed of our hospitality. We want you to stay here. The whole village invites you to stay. But here is what happened. My fourteenth nephew's second wife's uncle came over from White Cloud Market and he heard people say a crowd of men were on their way over here. They want to make trouble. What do you think? We have no firearms in this village and we do not know how to protect you."

Father Francis listened carefully to the old fellow. He threw his head back and laughed. "What kind of trouble will they make?" he asked. "Will they harm the village?"

"We don't know," replied the old man. "They may. If they find you here, they might burn the place down. Depends on what the Brahmins told them. They will probably make plenty trouble for all of us."

"But if I go away, will they let you alone?" pursued the missioner.

The old man hesitated. "Perhaps," he answered after a pause. "We will tell them you went away and we don't know where you are. We don't think they will do anything. We know most of them. But you might run right into them. My grandson's maternal cousin's husband said —."

"Take it easy," cut in the missioner. He had heard enough from the apologetic old man. "I was going home, anyhow," he added, "so don't worry about me." He hastily said his last few words of thanks and encouragement to the villagers and threw a final pleasantry at the wide-eyed children. A minute later he was outside the village stockade and on the little path.

Father Francis had no plan. But he had a little rosary, a great confidence in God and a very light heart. He did not see a single passer-by as he started out; the path was deserted. There was still some daylight left, but it was not going to remain long. He would put as much distance as he could between himself and the village while it lasted. If he encountered anybody —. He smiled — and wondered himself just what he would do. He had half a mind to give his pursuers a good tongue-lashing and see what would happen. If he did not meet them soon, it would be dark and that would make the situation much more awkward. Hard to impress people you cannot see, especially if they cut you down before you can open your mouth. He was probably going to get lost on these strange paths before long, anyhow. Well, he had his rosary to keep him company. And God would provide.

The light was dimming as the path entered the little grove of trees that he had admired that afternoon on his trip over. He remembered it with pleasure, but he would now have to pick his way carefully in the gathering dark. Suddenly the sun was down, and in that land of no twilight all the light vanished with it as if by magic. In an instant he fell to feeling his way.

Some leaves brushed his face at the very moment when his quickened senses caught the sound of voices ahead. As he stood stock-still and listened, there came the sound of rustling bushes and the tramp of feet. "Nobody wanders around these villages like that at night," he thought in a flash. "They are very likely to be my friends." The leaves of the jutting branch were still caressing his face. He could just perceive the outline of the leafy arm where it joined an enormous trunk. "It's that big banyan," he whispered and caught the inviting limb in one quick leap.

He pulled himself up into the crotch. Branches were sticking out in all directions. He felt along the side of the trunk and found another stout branch head high. Following an impulse he swarmed up on it. There three big branches went out from the crotch, making a natural perch. He was in a bower. "Enough light for my purposes," he whispered to himself. "And not too much for you, my friends," he added, as the rustling in the underbrush grew louder. They were evidently having trouble keeping on the path and, judging from the sounds, could hardly be a hundred yards away.

Father Francis smiled as they passed almost directly under him. They had as much chance of finding him as if he had been in Goa. He heard some muttered curses and then they were gone. He debated what to do. It was too late to continue the journey home. He would surely get lost — and would start all the dogs of the countryside barking and baying from here to Travancore. Might as well stay where he was. "Good place to say the rosary," he murmured. He slapped a mosquito. "And these little pests will help me to keep awake and say it."

It was a pale and tired missioner, but a serene and smiling one, who woke up John Vaz the next morning an hour after dawn. The young Portuguese jumped up with an unwonted haste. "Father, I am glad to see you!" he ejaculated. "I was terribly worried about you. They said last night a crowd had gone over there to catch you. I was scared."

Father Francis looked at the young man with sober gravity. "John," he said, "you were partly right. I did have a little trouble. The village people were very kind, but the poor souls had no place for me to stay. And I did not know of a single inn in the neighborhood. So that had me rather up a tree."

"But where in the world did you stay, Father?" asked the mystified man. "That's what I was wondering about."

Father Francis was already at the door. He turned for a moment. "John," he said, "hurry up and wash your face, won't you? It's time for Mass."

PERFECT HIDEOUT

DOWN the dusty street of Malacca came the familiar figure. His cassock was greenish and threadbare, its patches obvious and many; but the countenance above it was merry. A little bell tinkled in his hand as he passed along, shouting out over and over his strident call, much like a street hawker peddling his wares.

And he was in truth a hawker, this young Spanish priest, selling for nothing a pearl of great price in the streets of the city. "Christians," he shouted, "send the children to the church." Francis Xavier was calling the tiny people to prayer.

They came running, flocking, tumbling over each other, scampering around the Padre, dancing up to secure his recognition, clinging to his worn-out cassock. Singly and in groups, some chattering like magpies and others marching solemnly along, on came the procession cluttering up the street — little Portuguese, Malays, Indians, all the various strains that herded together in that early meeting-ground of East and West; white, yellow, brown, black; plump and skinny; grown children and babies; boys and girls.

Many had already gathered at the church; its shady portico spilled children in all directions; sitting, standing, playing, jumping, running.

One Malay maid of six had an interested group around her as she solemnly stirred an imaginary pot of rice, consisting of a bit of broken crockery filled with sand. This was set up on a pile of stones under which a brisk fire was supposed to crackle, an illusion which she conscientiously maintained by tossing in an occasional small stick for fuel. At intervals she ladled out portions of her make-believe concoction, and handed them around with elaborate bows to her admiring circle. Delighted shouts of appreciation arose from the favored banqueters. "Good to eat! Good to eat!" was the cry, as they went through the pantomime of tasting the magic sand.

Another group was composed of a half dozen boys who were dangling bits of string on the end of bamboo poles into a ditch by the side of the church. They appeared to be under the persuasion that the little depression contained a rushing torrent filled with fishes, which they were yanking out by great expenditures of energy and skill.

One sizable Portuguese youngster, in fact, must have considered the improvised aquarium to be nothing less than the great ocean, and himself engaged in combat with a whale, to judge from the amazing contortions and continual shouting that accompanied his struggles to land the fancied prey.

But these and other games broke up as the priest appeared with his reinforcements, and the gamesters joined the flock that already clamored around him. He smiled on them all, and without more ceremony shooed his whole collection into the church like a lot of little chicks.

Soon all were in their places, crowding the pews, sitting on the kneelers, the floor, perching where they could. Francis Xavier, after herding them in, walked to the sanctuary and stood looking over his following. He beamed on them and they all smiled back at him.

90

Many of them were little more than babies, sitting there putting their rosary beads in their mouths and looking up at the Padre with big, round eyes. Then there were the squirmers. Those at this interesting age made up the bulk of the gathering. Finally a good sprinkling had attained the solemnity of their first self-consciousness.

The system devised by the priest was to pick out a likely youngster, and have him lead the prayers and the recitation of the catechism. The clear treble of one of themselves gave the rest confidence. Often he selected the head squirmer for this office. He found that such a one usually had a good deal of energy to put into the recitation, and could thus be kept from expending it in distractions.

Such a leader was not hard to discover that morning. It was the erstwhile catcher of whales, who had now ensconced himself far in the back of the church, where he appeared to be sitting on tacks, and was attracting almost as much attention as Xavier himself.

"Paul Gomez, come up here." The surprised boy ceased his gyrations. "I mean you, Paul Gomez," repeated the priest.

Suddenly sheepish, Paul extricated himself from a knot of huddled children, and lumbered up the aisle. Like most boys of his age, Paul was a lion in his own world whose haunts and customs he knew; but a lamb — and today a badly frightened one — when suddenly projected onto that mysterious stage usually reserved for the inexplicable actions of grown-ups.

Xavier had a way all his own. That rare smile and gentle voice robbed Paul of his terror almost at once. "You would like to go fishing?" he asked the boy. Paul smiled and admitted he would. "So I thought," said Father Francis. "Well, let's go fishing, you and I. I'll tell you how."

After the few words of explanation and an encouraging pat on the back, Paul forgot the crowded church. He saw only the smiling eyes that bent over him. Courage came. He took the catechism, and read the first question and response in a loud, clear voice. The chorus of the answering children boomed out. He read the next — and the next. The lesson swung along. Paul had made his bow as the leader of the recitations.

The lessons were frequent — daily when Father Francis could find the time — and Paul became a fixture in his new position. All went well until the day of the final lesson. Father Francis was to leave Malacca soon. They said he was start- ing on a long and dangerous voyage to the far islands of Japan. Before leaving, he wanted to have a final, big meet- ing. It was to be in the cathedral and all the children had to attend. Not only that, but a lot of grown-up people were to be there also; as the idea was to let them witness the progress of the children, and perhaps be moved to emulate them.

Paul pondered all this in his heart. Paul flinched. He had become somewhat accustomed to his role of leading the prayers; yet always beforehand he felt a certain trepidation that never quite left him until he stood close to Father Francis and felt the support of that encouraging presence. This meeting in the cathedral was rather too much — in front of a lot of grown people and everything. Never would he be able to do it. He would have to try to hide or something. His anxious mind dwelt on wild schemes of escape.

The day came, and there appeared no feasible way to avoid going to the cathedral. His own father and mother were going! He hardly dared try to elude them. He trudged along disconsolately by their side. He showed no enthusiasm at the remarks of his parents, expressing their anticipated interest. He regarded the passers-by with malevolence during the rare moments when he took his glance off the ground under his feet, which he heartily wished would open and swallow him up.

Yet hope springs eternal in a boy's heart, and Paul was by no means resigned supinely to his fate. The busy little mind was alert. He still hoped to seize upon some straw.

The cathedral was jammed to the doors. Paul's heart sank at the sight of the crowd. If he could only run away, or get lost somewhere! How in the world could he ever face that crowded church, and recite the catechism? It was not to be thought of. The very cause of his desperation suddenly inspired him with a possible solution. The crowd was so great that he could easily get lost in it. He would hide in the back. He would get well out of sight, behind a lot of people where the crowd was thickest. Father Francis would never find him.

His father and mother went to the side aisle. Paul himself was supposed to go up to the front part, reserved for the children. Instead, he ducked hastily into the baptistry. There was a great press of people even there. He got behind them all.

In addition, the baptistry was a side wing, out of the line of vision from the sanctuary. Father Francis could not possibly locate him here. He would have to see through a lot of people, and around a corner besides! Paul breathed almost freely. He felt safe at last.

Soon it was time to begin. Father Francis looked over the

gathering, and decided that the place could not hold any more. Then he looked for his leader of the prayers. Strange, he was not in his accustomed place. The missioner began to call out. "Paul Gomez, Paul Gomez," rang through the church. No answer. Apparently Paul Gomez, wherever he was, did not hear.

Paul did hear, however, and only too well. And the more he heard, the more he crouched down and made himself small behind the backs of the throng in the baptistry. The calling stopped. Paul breathed a sigh of relief.

"He surely cannot find me; he will get somebody else," thought Paul consolingly to himself; and his suspense relaxed. He straightened up — to gaze into the smiling face of Father Francis!

"What is the matter, Paul? Going back on me?" sounded the pleasant, but now dreaded, voice.

Paul was too astonished to know what to say. "How did you know I was here?" he finally stammered. "I was afraid, and I thought you would not see me."

The missioner laughed. "So you thought I would lose my leader that easily, did you? Why, Paul, I *had* to find you; I have been counting on you. Come along now. Don't you want to help me out? It's easy. Just read as you always do. I'll stand right by you."

The missioner's hand stole into his; the sparkling eyes that always gave him confidence were beaming into his own. Paul suddenly forgot the crowd. His conscious world dwindled to two people — himself and the loved figure beside him. Clinging to that hand there could be nothing to fear.

They walked to the front of the church. Paul seized the

94

book, and at the customary signal sang out the Sign of the Cross. His voice rang clear. The whole church repeated it. He started the first prayer. The answer came back in a mighty wave. Calmly he went through the whole recitation. All his fear had vanished.

And always the reassuring smile and encouraging nod of Father Francis were there, carrying him along, instilling the balm that soothed the brave little heart so sorely agitated but a few minutes before.

"Well done, Paul," came the words he loved to hear, when the recitation was over; and Paul realized with quiet elation that he had got through the ordeal creditably. "Well done. I knew you would do it well."

"I don't mind the reading when I am with you, Father," replied Paul.

After a while, when the church had emptied, Paul sidled up to his friend again. "How did you find me, Father?" he asked.

"That was easy," replied Francis Xavier. "I knew you were going to be a good Jesuit some day; and that meant that when you wanted to hide, you would be clever enough to pick out the very best place to do it in. So I simply went to it, and there you were!"

And so it turned out. For the first vocation that Malacca gave to the Society was little Paul Gomez, who used to lead the prayers for the children of the East at the bidding of Father Francis.

THE GAMBLER

THE heart of Captain Rodriguez was kind, but his eyebrows were very bushy. As he sat at the head of the table he looked capable of almost anything but easy conversation. As a matter of fact his aspect did not belie him much, for with him, as with many seafaring men, the art of conversation consisted in volunteering copious remarks when he felt like it, and saying nothing at all when he didn't. To questions he was particularly impervious, and is it any wonder? The unintelligent remarks of landsmen passengers are indeed one of the trials of a seaman's life. Besides, in those days when Portugal was carving out an empire in the East, a man had enough on his mind in trying to sail a brig safely through the Indian Seas without the additional burden of entertaining passengers.

The Captain found his new passenger a bit more trying than usual. Senhor Garcia was a cut above the rough freebooters who largely made up the sixteenth-century passenger lists, and Captain Rodriguez knew this, but it worried him very little. He had carried all sorts of passengers, from the Governor down, and he was little disposed to waste ceremony on Senhor Garcia, whose remarks had already bored him.

"As I was saying, Captain, it's a pity really that we do not send out more representative men to these countries. I should surely hate to meet some of your passengers in a dark alley. Half of them would probably slit a man's gullet for a stiver. Why, even that priest on board is scarcely better than the rest. All he does is hobnob with the soldiers. Actually, I saw him gambling with them. Who is he, anyway? One expects more freedom out here than at home in Portugal, of course; but I must say that is carrying it a bit far. No wonder we are not converting the East very fast, if we are sending out gamblers as missionaries."

Bushy eyebrows and a gruff voice turned to the speaker.

"I've carried him on a good many trips, and we think he's a good sort. But you may be right. The Padre is surely a gambler. Keep your eye on him, and you'll see some high stakes. Good night!"

If Garcia was a bit nonplussed by this answer, it did not dull his critical faculties in the least, and the very next day he saw his opinion of the missionary confirmed. The soldiers were at their usual card game on the deck, and the priest could be observed, apparently one of the number. He did not really look much like a gambler. He was a Spaniard with a tall well-knit figure, a singularly open countenance, and dark eyes that now glowed, now melted, when closely seen. Yet he seemed quite at home among the soldiers, and they, as rough a lot as ever appeared on land or sea, apparently thought the world of him. The Padre was not playing, however, but was merely bantering with the crowd as the game went on. Strangely enough, the usual profanity that marked the soldiers' play was absent.

Suddenly one of the players pushed back his chair and staggered to his feet. The game had gone against him. The Padre followed him to the rail.

"Are you hard-hit, old man?"

97

"I'm finished. I haven't got a piastre left. There's nothing left but to go over the side."

"Oh, it's not as bad as all that. It will probably do you good. I warned you. Your money is gone, but that is a good lesson for you," counseled the missionary. He could not understand the appearance of deep despair that had settled over the poor fellow.

"Padre, you don't understand. I lost all my own money last week. This is the Commandant's money that he trusted me to take to the garrison at Malacca. I've lost the whole fifty reals."

This was bad, undoubtedly very bad — to have lost a sum of trust-money, and a large sum at that. It would go hard with the unfortunate fellow at the end of the trip. It was a poser even for the Padre, but not for long.

"Wait here a moment, old man. I think I can help you. I'm something of a gambler myself."

It was not long before the missionary was back, and he had some gold pieces in his hands.

"Here we are. I've borrowed this from a friend on the boat. Let's try our luck again. But first you've got to promise me two things: that if we win you will give up gambling, and that you will make your peace with God in the sacred tribunal. Is it a bargain?"

Incredulity chased despair off that rough countenance, and was followed in turn by beaming relief.

"Promise! Padre, I promise anything. Of course, I'll do what you say. If I can only get the money back to fulfill my trust, I'll never touch a card again."

The game was still in progress, and Senhor Garcia was still an interested spectator. This time he saw the missionary

98

actually take the cards in his hands as the soldiers resumed play, and cut them for luck — or was it the Sign of the Cross that the graceful hand formed over them? The game went on, and the soldier appeared to be regaining his losses while the missionary stood by encouraging him. Senhor Garcia had seen enough by this time, and he turned away to reflect on the need of representative men; although if he had waited a bit longer he might have seen the Padre sternly order his friend from the game when he had recovered his misused funds.

Captain Rodriguez was in a more genial mood when Senhor Garcia met him the next day. Small wonder, for his anxious navigation through practically uncharted seas was successfully over, and the ship was about to cast anchor at Malacca.

"Come ashore with me, Senhor Garcia," invited the bluff old man. "You've never been out East before. Come along with me to the praya, and you will have no trouble getting settled somewhere."

Most of the passengers had already gone ashore by the time Captain Rodriguez and Senhor Garcia were ready to disembark and start for the town. In those days the town of Malacca lay at some distance from the anchorage, and was reached by a fairly long walk along a wooded road. A pleasant walk it was, too, for this pair after their arduous voyage. It was interrupted suddenly. They heard a commotion in the trees by the roadside. The Captain peered through the brush.

"Well, by all that's holy!" he exclaimed. The bushy eyebrows grew stern, but could not hide a soft light in the honest sailor's eyes.

"Take a look at this, Garcia," he whispered to his companion.

The sight that met Garcia's eyes was unusual enough. The missioner of the boat was on his knees striking himself with a discipline made of iron chains. Beside him was his soldier friend of the boat, begging him to desist. "I'll do penance. I'll do penance," the soldier was saying. Garcia looked and tiptoed away.

"That's your friend the gambler," chuckled the Captain, "and that's his trump card you see him playing. I told you he played for high stakes. He cured that chap of cards on the ship, but I heard he failed to get his confession. But he always wins, and it looks as if the game is his."

It was a crestfallen Garcia who turned to the hearty old salt.

"I'm sorry," he said. "I completely misjudged him. Who is he, anyhow?"

"Around these parts," said Captain Rodriguez, "many people call him 'the Saint.' His name is Francis Xavier."

ISLAND ROSE

THE people of Amboina knew what they wanted. Heaven knows it wasn't much. A blue denim tunic to keep off the sun and a nipa roof to keep off the rain were about the sum of human desires in the Spice Islands. However, right here was the rub. There wasn't any rain to keep off. There had not been any for a long time. That might have seemed to simplify their needs even more by dispensing with the laborious and continuous patching of their flimsy castles of straw; but it didn't. It complicated things — very much so. For there was one other need even more constant and serious. It was the need of a full stomach.

In Amboina this problem was usually fairly simple. The blue sea girting the little isle was full of fish that yielded a heavy toll to the daring fishermen with their tiny barques and enormous nets. The hillsides were covered with the heavy fronds of wild plantain bushes whose fruit was theirs for the picking. The lordly coconut palms and the dainty little umbrella-like papaya trees that fringed the sandy shore-lines also supplied a substantial part of their larder. But man, no matter what glorious simplicity he may inherit or attain, does not live on fish and fruit — at least not willingly. The food of man is grain. And therefore the people of Amboina were not thrilled by the big hauls of fish, and they turned up their noses contemptuously at the piles of coconuts and

101

plantains that the women and children were gathering at will. There was no rain. And there lay their pride and joy, the ricefields, the bearers of the precious grain, parched and scorching in the sun.

The ricefields! How their hopes and fears, their very lives, were bound up in those green squares that dotted the little isle. With what care they marked them out and delimited them by the little ditches that would at the same time conduct the precious water to the thirsty roots and also jealously safeguard them from the encroachments of equally rice-obsessed neighbors. And the labor that was so prodigally expended on them! There was the first rough ploughing, when to turn over the heavy clods with the rude wooden share taxed even the powerful water buffaloes; the lighter but more meticulous task of harrowing; the laborious round of the treadmill that raised enough water from the scanty brooks to flood the ground; and finally the back-breaking job of wading about up to the waist in the mud to transplant the green shoots from the forcing-beds. After that it was merely a question of heaven's bounty in sending the proper weather. If the sky let fall the later rains to nourish the green blades and kept off the high winds that beat them flat, nothing could interfere with their precious yield in due time. But when heaven withheld the precious moisture, vanished was the dear vision of golden grain. Hopes and dreams faded and failed. The chief business of life had gone awry. Heaven was blind or at least dry. No rain, no rice. Amboina was in the depths.

Rose Ramdeen was as worried as anybody else, but she got a little tired listening to the jeremiads of the men. Being a woman, she was a realist and so spent more time in gathering fruit than in lamenting rice, on the principle of looking the situation in the face. Being a Christian woman, she had her own ideas about the withholding of the blessed rain from the island that could remain so sunk in sin and superstition after knowing the true doctrine. For the test of the prolonged drought had been too much for the faith of many, and they had reverted to worshiping the idols as a last chance to in-voke the rain.

Some days before, the head men of the village had taken old Dyaus, the harvest god, out in solemn procession. "Going to let him see how badly the rice needs rain," they said. Rose and a few other women crossed themselves and prayed and scoffed. "Fine chance to get rain from that fat old wooden fellow," they jeered. "Now we shall never get any rain. This is offending God. Can any happiness come from it?" But the faithful few made little headway. Great crowds joined the procession.

Rose went home sad, and being an Amboina woman said little, for in that commonwealth it fell to the lot of the men to speak words and regulate affairs. At least, such was the time-honored custom and established theory. Actually, of course, the women of Amboina, as elsewhere, said more than their prayers; but it was among themselves, over the cooking pots, rather than in the Councils of State. So Rose worried and prayed and kept her counsel, as she cooked a measure of the precious, dwindling rice for the supper that was to greet her husband returning with the fishing-fleet that night.

"John," said Rose, after listening for a half hour to his recital of what had happened during the fishing expedition, "the rice isn't going to last much longer. If no rain comes and the new crop is lost, we will have to live on plantains."

John knew this only too well. The prospect was not pleasing. He began to grumble, as is the fashion of his kind. In the middle of his tirade, he suddenly remembered a piece of news he had to impart. "By the way, we passed a boat coming from Ternate this morning. They say it is coming here and has a priest aboard. Maybe he can ask God to send us some rain or something. I can't think of any other way to get it."

"John! A priest coming here! Why didn't you tell me?" The usually placid Rose was excited. It was indeed a piece of news. Malacca was far away; its merchants came seldom to Amboina; its priests were few and came even more rarely still. Actually the island had not seen a priest for five years. Rose was elated. "Are you sure there is a priest aboard? He came at a good time. Did you know the people took the idol out of the temple last week and all worshiped it? There was an immense crowd. Lots of Christians too. I saw people from all of our seven Christian villages. I was ashamed. People offending God; no rain coming. Isn't that so?"

John agreed. "Am I going fishing with idols to protect me?" he asked of the roof and all the nooks and corners of the house, looking everywhere but at Rose. This was the manner of his people, whose favorite form of locution is the rhetorical question addressed to the four winds of heaven. "Where would I have been in that last typhoon if that greasy old idol was protecting me? Feeding fishes instead of catching them. If it wasn't the Star of the Sea protected me, who did? I am asking you. As for me, I am praying to God and His Mother. These people will not enjoy happiness."

"That isn't all," put in Rose. "That old Mr. Ahmed who speaks the words in Sandy Bank Village wasn't satisfied with a procession. He insisted on setting the idol up right beside the ricefields. Said he had to see how dry it was. And the crazy women are all burning incense and —"

"How can he see without eyes?" broke in John. "And what could he do if he did see? Better take the old rascal out and throw him in the river. He needs a bath anyhow. That's all the water he will ever see," expostulated the blunt fisherman. Then suddenly, surprised to find himself saying something clever, his eyes strayed for confirmation to his wife, who now stood over the fire infusing the tea. The glow of the firelight that has a way of enhancing dusky beauty played over his personable Rose. She turned big, luminous eyes to his. They smiled in a rare and fugitive moment of mind meeting mind.

"John, how clever. It's a wonderful idea. If the old idol can't give us any water for the rice, we can give him some for a bath. He needs it, after all the incense these stupid women are burning in his sooty old face. Maybe we can tell the priest. Here is tea. You are tired. I wonder if it's the same priest who came last time. He could not speak our Amboina words. Anyhow we can see tomorrow."

John took his ease while Rose pottered about the little tasks of the Amboinese housekeeper. Her heart swelled at the manifestation of staunch faith on the part of the simple fisherman who shared her lot, as the heart of woman never fails to do at any revelation of goodness in a man — perhaps because it has learned to expect rather the opposite from the lumbering and inexplicable creatures. Rose was happy.

A spare but wiry foreigner, with a merry face and a dilapidated cassock, was seen on the beach of Amboina the next morning. It was Francis Xavier on his first visit to the island. He had picked up a few words of the language on the trip over and had a simple greeting for the people who welcomed him warmly as he went about, poking into the villages, smiling an entree for himself, laughing and playing with the children. There was a young catechist from Malacca with him who knew the island patois well. He explained that Father Francis wanted them all to come to the chapel for catechism. They all promised. They were genuinely glad to see the priest. And this one was so kind to the children. The little ones loved him already. And this was a key to the heart of Amboina — as it is, indeed, to the affection of any people who themselves love those little strayed angels entrusted to them by an all-wise God.

In spite of the hearty welcome, Xavier was not long on his rounds before he heard about the recent serious defection of the little flock. "Well, we shall see what can be done," he answered calmly to the complaints of the few scandalized faithful ones. "Don't be too hard on the people. The priest comes seldom and they had no chance to learn much doctrine." There was a twinkle in his eye when he added, "I do not see any rain falling. Apparently the idol has failed to meet the situation. But," seriously again, "it is a great offense against God and we must put a stop to it."

There was a commotion on the edge of the crowd. A young woman pushed her way forward. The spirited Rose had forgotten the inhibition of island custom. "Father," she burst out amid the group of men, "the women won't stop their incantations and incense-burning. We told them it was no use, but they say they must do it until the rain comes. No rain comes. I told them they were keeping the rain away by offending God, but their hearts are not opened.

Maybe the Father has some means to make them stop."

Father Francis looked at the indignant little person who was taking on herself the solicitude of the island Church. His heart warmed. He had listened attentively to her little speech and found in it the idea for which he had been search-ing in this quandary.

"Did they say they would not stop until it rains? Go tell them for me it won't rain until they stop."

"Father, will you ask God to send the rain? I'll tell them you promise —"

"I cannot command the rain, my child. Only God can do that. I do not know His will. But I promise you He will not let the rain fall to strengthen their superstitious fear of this foolish idol. You go tell them no repentance, no rain. I want them to destroy the idol. After that, we will see if God will forgive this offense and send rain. After all, He is not very angry, for this is more ignorance than malice on the part of our good people."

"Father, surely." Rose was all eagerness. "I am going." She lingered. Her husband's sarcastic reference to the idol on the night before popped into her mind. "Must the idol be destroyed, Father? How would it be to give him a duck-ing in the river? My husband said since the idol cannot give us any water for the rice it is best for us to give him some by a good bath. Then at least he will know what water is."

The missioner smiled again. This little person would make a good missioner herself, he thought. She certainly did not lack ideas. "Excellent," he said beaming. "That is a good plan. The punishment will fit the crime. Go and suggest a bath for the bogus rainmaker."

Rose found the main offenders crestfallen and chastened

by the failure of their panicky superstitions. A week had passed and the sky was as brassy as ever. A spark of faith lurking somewhere in their rude hearts had rendered them a bit uneasy from the start. The arrival of the priest intensified this feeling. The dominating Rose had little trouble with them. Only a few old hags hesitated. Rose talked them all down, and finally to end it all, in a burst of enthusiasm, she shouted to them gleefully, "Come on, now! Let us take the idol and show him what water is, since he evidently does not know. He can't send any water, so let us give him a bath in it. That will teach him a lesson."

Humor in a spring of action is like a match in powder. It was all over with the idol from that moment. One woman smiled, another laughed out loud. Good-bye, idol. The pack sprang on him as one, and amid the cackles and jeers of his former worshipers, he was ingloriously shuffled into the watery sanctuary that was to be his first bath and his last resting place.

Father Francis disclaimed all credit for the rain that fell the next day, although the catechist reported that his master's bed was untouched, and he must have spent the whole night in prayer. "God rewards those who trust in Him," said the missioner, to the delighted community that gathered around him in the chapel at the hour of catechism. "And for even one or two faithful ones He will always do great things."

The dusky complexions of Rose and John were not susceptible to blushes, but at this reference they performed the Amboinese equivalent of gazing at the ground. The happy crowd milled about in a common ecstasy. Outside a lowering sky was letting fall the cloudburst that would save the rice.

108

TYPHOON

THE junk sailed out of the harbor bravely enough. The breeze was moderate and the motion of the queer craft not unpleasant, as it slid up and down, dipping gently into the long swells. The little group of passengers stood on the raised deck watching the outlines of Malacca fade in the distance. They saw a late June sunset flinging its shafts of color over the bay. The glowing panorama raised their spirits.

"Thou hast put on praise and beauty, and art clothed with light as a garment" (*Ps.* 103:2), murmured one of the watching men, more to himself than to his companions. He stood aside from the rest a little, musing on the scene. Good-bye, Malacca. It was not the best way to set out for a long sea voyage. Japan must be a very long distance away. Would they ever reach it? When he first saw the forbidding hulk of the battered old Chinese junk and the huge, clumsy, patched sails, he began to doubt it. The reek and the Stygian darkness of the ship's interior made him doubt even more. Could they live in such a place? Well, he and Father Torres and Brother Fernandez would have to try it and find out. Anjiro and Emmanuel and Amador did not seem to mind it, but of course they had been on junks before.

It might have been better to take a Portuguese ship, but they could not wait forever. The Chinese ship at least was going somewhere. It was not going to be a cruise for comfort, but no help for that. What a villainous-looking crew on board! If any group of seamen ever looked ready for every rascality, they were the men. And the good captain was a pirate by profession — or at least so it was said. Not too reassuring. Yet all things work together for those who love God; so what did it matter? Better not borrow trouble. Might all turn out to be providential in the end. Anyhow, they were going with God. And for God. It was His business to see that they got to Japan.

"Father Francis, Father Francis!" came a call from the group huddled near the little deckrail. The musing man turned to his companions. They chatted a moment. They started to say the rosary together, to ask the blessing of Mary Immaculate on their perilous voyage to Japan.

The smile of the Star of the Sea seemed to be on the voyage for the first weeks. The heat was intense, but the south-west monsoon blew steadily, and the little ship dipped and wallowed along. The missioners soon learned to spend as little time as possible in the stifling forecastle where their crude bunks had been arranged. They talked, lounged and prayed on deck most of the time, or just sat on empty pig crates and watched the long green waves swelling and swirling in the ship's wake. From stem to stern every inch of the junk was foul and disorderly; the odors alone drove everybody to the deck. Yet when the call came for the simple meals of rice and tea and salted fish, the missioners steeled themselves to ignore the smells and crowded around the murky cookstove to eat their bowls with the rest.

They had little but their own companionship. Nobody knew any Chinese but Emmanuel, and his years in Goa and Malacca had erased from his mind all but a few crude sentences of his little-known village dialect. Among the seamen only the Captain knew Portuguese, and he did not seem to be a man for much speaking in any language. He was seen often with his little daughter. What possessed him to bring her on such a rough voyage nobody knew. His wife and the rest of his family had remained in Malacca. But he seemed very much attached to the child, and she spent a lot of her time skipping around the junk calling "Ah Pa" and looking for him. The missioners did not succeed in getting very well acquainted with the little miss. Smiles and pantomime were their only means of communication. Yet the mere presence of the pert little sprite in her diminutive satin trousers and pigtails brought some cheer to the dull monotony of the long weeks on the sea.

If the Captain of the junk was a pirate, he was a pious one in his own way. When he was not lounging or asleep in his little cubby-hole of a cabin, he seemed to spend most of his time fidgeting around the shrine he had fixed up in the fore-castle. It was an elaborate one. In the center, right beside the ladder to the upper deck, was a big idol of Ma Chu, the goddess of sailors. With her were two assistants, ranged on either side of her — Favorable Wind Ear and Thousand Mile Eye. Apparently the Captain counted heavily on their aid for the success of the voyage. He was constantly kowtowing before them and replenishing the pots of incense. Sometimes he placed bits of cooked meat and small cups of rice wine before them. He never bothered to brush the cobwebs off them or to clean off the smudge that blackened their grotesque faces. It pained the missioners to witness the misdirected religious gropings of the poor man, and it wrung them most of all to see him teaching his little daughter to carry out the

111

same form of worship. The tiny child accompanied her father in many of these performances. She seemed equally familiar with the prostrations, bows and implorations that characterized them.

Father Torres was not reassured by these constant invocations of supposedly benign spirits that had no real existence. He feared they might involve some connection with malignant spirits whose existence was only too real. In seeking light on the subject from Emmanuel, he learned from the Chinese boy that all Chinese sailors were much devoted to the same practice, that he would see plenty of it, and that he had better get used to it. "This is mild," said Emmanuel. "Wait until some trouble comes, and then you will see all of them doing it. They won't make a move without worshiping the idols and casting lots to find out what is the lucky thing to do. They think everything depends on pleasing the spirits. This is the custom."

The travelers often talked about the prospects of the strange voyage. Optimism was not the keynote, as all realized that anything could happen. Emmanuel and Amador proved typical sons of the Orient in always expecting the worst as a matter of course, but they were also typical in not being the least bit disturbed by their own gloomy expectations. Anjiro was more sanguine, as befitted a man setting out for his own country, but he showed no great enthusiasm for the way they had chosen to get there. Brother Fernandez worried the least of all, except for Father Francis. He — as far as anyone could see — did not worry at all. It was he who always calmed the little anxieties and excitations of the others.

Once he spoke seriously to Father Torres. "We must not

lose our confidence in God, Father," he said. "He sent us on this trip. It's true the conditions are not ideal. The junk is uncomfortable but it seems seaworthy. The Captain and some of his crew are pirates, and the whole lot are very superstitious. That is a pity, but the poor fellows do not know any better, so what can you expect? These are the conditions God has provided for us. You may be sure He can bring some good out of them. Let's trust in Him and thank Him for getting us to Japan."

The sun was terrifically hot, but the sea breeze was a great alleviation. It was on a torrid night of the third week in July when they suddenly realized that the wind had completely stopped. The heat was so stifling in the dead calm that nobody slept. The voyagers tossed and perspired all night. The next morning they all had slight headaches. The sea lay glassy and calm in the broiling sun. The junk seemed scarcely to move. There was a feeling of depression, as if the world had suddenly stood still. The air was heavy. They all passed the day listlessly in the sweltering heat.

Instead of putting out more sail to catch any little puff of occasional wind, the sailors took all the sails in. Then they went around shifting cargo, fastening the hatches and closing every tiny porthole. That made the ship even more stifling than it was before. It was late afternoon when they finished their work.

The missioners had viewed these preparations in puzzlement. They were lounging on the deck when the sky got a little dark prematurely. It was only five o'clock. Suddenly there was a strong little puff of wind accompanied by a few scattering raindrops.

Emmanuel jumped as if a gun had gone off. "The big

113

wind," he shouted. "It's coming. Everybody down below."
His Oriental calm had completely vanished. He was excited. He ran to Father Francis. "Make them hurry," he
implored. "Very important."

The missioners saw no reason for haste. And they were
reluctant to return to the stuffy cabin. But Emmanuel was
insistent. He pushed and herded them to the ladder. It was
well he did so. Brother Fernandez had just seized the ladder
when a gust of wind suddenly came from nowhere that almost tore loose his hold. He scrambled down as another
gust came and then another. Before the others could follow,
the deck was swept with a raging wind that beat on the ship
as if to tear it apart. A heavy driving rain lashed at their
faces. They needed no urging now. They clung carefully
to the ladder and made their way down. The ship was already pitching so that it was almost impossible to keep on
their feet. They got on all fours to crawl to their bunks.

Emmanuel was the last to come down the ladder. Father
Francis did not see him descend. He scanned the faces of
his little huddled group in the murky light. Emmanuel was
not there. Father Francis started to crawl back along the
companionway to look for him, when suddenly the junk gave
a violent lurch. He heard a startled gasp from somewhere,
and then a dull thud sounded. Back in the stern of the junk
where there was nothing but the open hold with the narrow
catwalk around it, something or somebody had fallen. Father
Francis scrambled in the direction of the sound. He peered
into the inky depths of the hold but could see nothing. He
heard only the lapping of the bilge water that sloshed around
in the bottom of the hold. He hesitated a moment. Suddenly

114

from the darkness below came a peculiar sound like a low moan.

"There's a man down there!" In his excitement Father Francis forgot that the Chinese sailors crouched around in the forecastle understood hardly a word of Portuguese. Nobody stirred. He stood erect and ran to the nearest group huddled outside the Captain's cabin. He shouted and gesticulated. Neither his words nor his signs had any effect. The sailors ignored him with a curious stolidity, almost as if he did not exist. Frantic with the loss of time, he called to his companions. "Father Torres! Fernandez! Anjiro! Come quickly — all of you. A man fell in the hold. I think it's Emmanuel."

It was not easy to get down into the hold of the wallowing, shuddering ship, as the mountainous waves tossed it around, broke over it, and battered at it. Anjiro and Amador appealed to the sailors in the pidgin Malay that some of them knew, but they received only stony stares in reply. There was no stationary ladder into the hold. The young Japanese made his way down by clinging and climbing between bales of cargo like a cat. He stepped in water up to his knees. As it sloshed around him he saw a huddled form in the dim light. "It's Emmanuel," he shouted up. "I'm afraid he is drowned."

To raise the unconscious man and lift him to the level of the companionway was a painfully difficult task. Father Francis and Amador got down into the hold to help Anjiro, and between them all they managed to lift and tug the fallen man halfway up. Several times they almost fell in a heap together as the bales they clung to shifted with the rolling of the vessel. The other two leaned over the hatch to help

115

by pulling. Soon Brother Fernandez' strong arms got a grip on the dripping, inert form of Emmanuel, and with a final push and a pull he was up.

Emmanuel's low moans told them he was alive. "He would have drowned in that hold, if we had not got him out," said Anjiro. "In some places the water was up to my waist." They got his wet clothes off and wrapped him in a blanket.

Father Torres looked over the unconscious man for broken bones. He felt his pulse and his head. "Doesn't seem to be any fracture," he reported. "Probably got a concussion when he fell." Emmanuel opened his eyes as he spoke. He looked bewildered. Then he recognized them and tried to smile.

The missioners' relief was speedily interrupted. Suddenly there was a great commotion. They heard somebody shouting, and then the tramping and banging of the sailors as they began rushing here and there. The sea was pounding worse than ever. "What's the matter?" wondered Father Francis. "Is it abandon ship?" He did not speak his fear. Then somebody burst out in a dreadful wailing and crying. It went on and on. Something tragic must have happened.

Amador was not long in finding out what it was. He was out and back in an instant. "The Captain's daughter," he whispered, "fell overboard. A sailor saw her. Swept away immediately. Can't do a thing in this sea. That's the Captain doing the wailing." Amador paused to catch his breath. "They did not answer me politely," he added. "Very surly and rough. Almost as if they thought we had something to do with it. But maybe it was only their excitement."

Father Francis and Anjiro went immediately to the scene

116

of the accident where the sailors were congregated. They looked at the darkling, surging waters and saw there was nothing to be done. There was no trace of the Captain's daughter; she must have been drowned in that raging sea almost at once. Father Francis said a prayer for the little maid. Then he turned to the Captain and said some words of sympathy in Malay. The Captain turned away from him and continued his bloodcurdling wails. The missioner repeated his words to the nearest sailors. Their only replies were angry stares.

When they returned to the cabin, Emmanuel was sitting up. He was dazed and shaky and he was also worried. He and Amador were talking in low tones. The Captain's wailing died down and presently they saw him go to the idol shrine. He lit some joss sticks. Emmanuel watched him, looking more worried than ever. "That's right," he whispered sarcastically. "Your old Favorable Wind Ear brought us right into a typhoon. And Thousand Mile Eye can't see where we are going. Now ask them what caused all the trouble, and they will probably tell you to blame it on us."

"What's the matter, Emmanuel? You should be thanking God you are alive. Is there any trouble?" Father Francis sensed the real concern in the boy's tones.

"Listen and I tell you to hear, Fathers and Brother." Emmanuel addressed the whole group. "It's bad about the Captain losing his daughter. China Sea people believe the spirits in the water do that. They believe the spirits are angry, when a storm gets stirred up. And if somebody is saved after they get their clutches on him, that makes them angrier still. Amador said the sailors would not help to pull me out of the hold. Of course not. That's because they

117

thought the Water Spirits had put their hands on me and would turn on them. Then when you rescued me, the spirits took the Captain's daughter instead. That's the way they think. And now the Captain is wondering if they are going to take the whole ship to the bottom. We are in a tight situation. Whatever happens is going to be blamed on us."

There was little sleep on the tossing ship that night for most people, and for Father Francis there was none at all. He urged the others to take what rest they could get, but for himself he decided it was a good time to watch and pray. If anything was to happen, he wanted to be ready for it. He took up his vigil right outside the sliding panel that served the little cabin for a door. The long night wore on. The Captain kept up his attentions to the idols off and on. At other times he went to join the muttering knots of sailors hanging around the galley. They conferred in low tones. Three times during the night a group walked past the missioners' cabin as if bent on some sudden errand, but they only made the circle of the forecastle and drifted back to the galley again. All three times they saw the strange, bearded figure of Father Francis standing like a statue. If they had any sinister designs, some force restrained them. They peered at the missioner, but they said nothing and passed on. When morning came they say him still standing in the same place, calm and erect in the gray dawn, like a sentinel on guard.

What the junk had encountered was the tail-end of a typhoon that had gone inland further up the coast. The wind abated the very next day. A lot of joss sticks had to be lit and meats offered to the idols before the Captain could decide what to do, but finally the ship weighed anchor and started to bear up the coast. The missioners breathed more

118

freely, as the junk got on its course again. They asked no questions. But they were disagreeably surprised when Emmanuel suddenly learned that the Captain had decided to stop at Sancian Island. That would mean an interminable delay. The idols advised it — such was the reason given. Father Francis had to do a lot of talking to the Captain. He finally persuaded the worried man that the Portuguese traders would make it hot for him, if he persisted in violating the agreement made with the Commandant of Malacca to proceed straight to Japan. The Captain grudgingly gave in.

The missioners thought their difficulties were over. After more weeks of sailing, the junk had left Sancian far behind and was rounding the turn to start up the China coast. But Ma Chu and her two precious assistants had not exhausted their capacity for making trouble. Just as it seemed clear-sailing to Japan, it was announced that the Captain had made another decision — this time to hole up in the port of Swatow for the winter! This was a ruinous plan. If they went into a Chinese port, when would they ever get out? But this time Father Francis could not persuade the Captain to change his mind. The idols had said so — the lots had given very clear indications — and in that port there were no Portuguese to fear. The little band of voyagers to Japan reverted to gloom. "Just when we had finished the worst part," remarked Anjiro, who took any interference with the trip to his native country as a personal injury. "If they do that, I fear we may never get to Japan."

"When you put out to sea with a pirate, what can you expect?" remarked Father Torres a little tartly. "There's no honor among thieves, you know. Between the rascally Captain and his wretched idols, how could the voyage have any good luck?"

"Easy. Take it easy." Father Francis was at his elbow. "What you say is true, but it leaves God out of the calculation. He can bring good out of evil. He can use any sort of means to get us to Japan — even worse means than these. Our good Captain is no doubt a pirate. But God is the real Captain of the ship. Have a little confidence. He will get us there yet."

The crew hailed a fishing-boat as they were nearing the harbor of Swatow that same evening. After some trouble, they managed to persuade the fishing-boat to pull up alongside the junk. A lot of shouting back and forth between the two boats went on for a long time. Finally the fishing-boat pulled away toward the harbor. Instead of following it in, the junk changed its course immediately and headed out to sea again. What had happened? The puzzled missioners deputed Emmanuel to go and find out.

Emmanuel had managed to cultivate a few acquaintances among his countrymen in the rough crew. He soon came back with the story. He wore a smile of satisfaction. "We are heading for Japan," he announced. "No more stops. We can't turn back to any South China port now, as the monsoon would be against us." He enjoyed the bewilderment on the missioners' faces. He slapped his thigh and laughed. "Why didn't we put into Swatow? Listen and I will tell you to hear. Pirates! The place is full of pirates! The Captain was afraid to go in. Those men in the fishing-boat were pirates also, but some of them were friends of the Captain. All pirates know each other, you see. It's good the Captain knew these people. If we had been strangers, they would

120

have told us to sail right in. They would have caught us all. There are several large bands congregated on shore and we should have had no chance."

"There's also a proverb that says: 'Set a thief to catch a thief,' you know," said Brother Fernandez slyly, nudging Father Torres. "Next thing you know we'll be in Kago-shima. This trip to Japan isn't turning out so badly, after all."

EMPTY NETS

THE crystal waters of the bay sparkled in the morning sun, and the boats caught part of its glory on their full-spread sails, as they filed out to the fishing grounds, with their bows spearing into the green swells and tossing high the silvery spray. It was a fairy picture. So might some splendid argosy of the mind's fancy appear — could it suddenly spring from dreams to reality and bodily form — to be wafted amid those sun-kissed isles on its quest of romantic mystery bent. But the people of Kagoshima had no eyes for the beauty of sky and sea and sail. For beauty cannot be eaten, and the bay, lovely as it might be, was yet lacking in a much more practical particular. Once teeming with fish, it had latterly failed to yield anything like its normal toll, and as a consequence its people, depending almost wholly upon their fishing as a means of livelihood, were seriously feeling the pinch. The catch was scarcely worth the taking. And this was strange enough, since for generations past the Bay of Kagoshima had always lived up fully to its cherished reputation as the best fishing grounds in Japan. But something was wrong. The fish simply did not seem to be there; the nets brought up little or nothing.

Gloom pervaded the group of villagers that watched the boats go out. Nobody said much. Nobody knew what to do. Some of the Elders advised laying up the boats for a space, arguing that the sea gods were obviously angry at something or somebody, and might possibly be appeased by such a humble gesture. They added the serious argument that the boats were taking nothing anyhow, so such a measure could not make matters any worse, and might make them better. But to forego the only chance of catching any fish was too much to ask of the more practical-minded boat-men. They continued to put out for the day's fishing, al-though in increasing pessimism, as each day only registered another failure. Prayers and sacrifices of all sorts were offered in the temples. Several of the villages had even marched their idols in solemn procession along the shore, so that their divinities could see for themselves the hard plight of Kagoshima and be moved perchance to rectify it. But all was to no avail. The situation got worse instead of better. From taking a few small fish, the fleet soon descended to catching almost nothing. Kagoshima was on the verge of despair.

Old man Yamanaka was of the opinion that the spirits of the water were offended at something, and had accordingly chased away the fish in order to punish the people. As chief Elder he had to pretend to have some opinion. This time the boats had returned before noon to report the usual luck. The fishermen had got so tired of their useless labor that they had lost heart and come home.

The meeting of the Elders was not a hopeful one. They had already held many. And they all ended in nothing. Yet something had to be said by somebody, so Yamanaka said it. "The spirits drove the fish away," he boomed pontifi-cally. "How else do you account for it? Always had fish in this bay. Suddenly look, not see. How explain? You think the fish just decide to go away by themselves? Fish are not so intelligent. Somebody chased them away. And that must be the spirit who lives in the water. Who else would do it? I am asking you." He paused. He had done his duty as chief Elder. He had said something; even offered an explanation. He knew he had not advanced the problem an iota. But still, why should he? Even an Elder has his limitations. He looked around in virtuous satisfaction.

"That sounds reasonable," spoke up his equally venerable and sententious crony, Mr. Hakimura. "Undoubtedly you are speaking true principles." Old Yamanaka bowed in deprecation of these compliments, but with an uneasy wonderment as to what might come next. His friend Hakimura was of a rather incisive turn of mind, with a reputation for asking embarrassing questions.

"But the question is not who chased them away," pursued Hakimura, getting down to his point. "It is rather to find some means to bring them back." This sentence voiced the sentiment of all, and a murmur of appreciation ran through the assembly. "Can the spirits bring them back? That is the question. Never mind who drove them away. Myself, I doubt if the spirits can bring them back. If they could, why wait so long? Have we not given them enough face? Burning incense in every temple. And we gave them food and money not a little. Even had a procession for them, so they could see our trouble for themselves. And many bonzes, and everybody kowtowing and prostrating. What was the use of it all? What more do they want? It's my opinion that the fish won't pay any attention to them."

The chief Elder listened uneasily to this speech. His own personal opinion was about the same, had he cared to express it. But his problem was a double one. Bringing back the fish was only part of it. The other part was to preserve the dignity and reputation of the chief Elder, whether the fish came back or not. The people looked to him as the principal hope of devising some means to bring back the fish. Much as he wanted to see the fish return, he was equally concerned in passing to somebody else the unenviable task of making them return. It was a job for the bonzes. Yamanaka grew more aggrieved the more he thought about it. Why should people expect him to bring back the fish? He did not profess to have any power over the depths of the sea. The bonzes did. Yet the more incantations, the less fish. His policy had been to put the whole blame on the spirits, and the whole hope on the bonzes, so that nobody would look to the chief Elder either in hope or blame.

Suddenly he saw the failure of the bonzes was letting him down. The people had to look to somebody, and they were swinging back to him. The last sentence kindled his anger. "Maybe the fish won't pay any attention to the spirits," he shouted. "But neither will they pay any to me. How in the world do all you people expect me to bring them back? Am I the king of the fish that I can order them around? These bonzes are the men who ought to do it. Where did all this money go that we spent in the temples? And still no fish. At least I agree with Mr. Hakimura on this point. Let us spend no more money on such foolishness."

The chief Elder having extricated himself in this fashion, the meeting was about to end in nothing, as was usual, when there was a curious interruption. An old graybeard who had listened a lot and said nothing suddenly took the floor. "There is a lot of talk about bringing the fish back," he said, waving a skinny arm and bending over impressively. "I do not know how to do that, and neither do you. But I have an idea as to what sent them away." He paused to let his words sink in. Every eye was riveted on him by this announcement. "You know that Anjiro family?" he continued. "Well, their eldest boy came home last week from foreign parts — away off in the South Seas somewhere. And that's not all. He brought a foreign devil with him!"

The audience saw his drift immediately. Most of them had heard of the Anjiro boy's returning. Some had heard there was a foreigner with him. But nobody had connected the unusual event with the disappearance of the fish. They were quite prepared to do so now, however, once it was suggested to them. The old man saw he had made an impression. "There's the reason our fish went away!" he shouted triumphantly. "Talk about bad omens! Do you want a worse one than that?" He sat down.

A murmur of approbation soon swelled to an excited clamor, as the new solution took hold on minds so long baffled to find one. The meeting abandoned parliamentary rules; everybody began to talk at once. "It's absolutely certain that this is the cause," asserted one old Elder, who had so far distinguished himself by offering no explanation or solution of any kind. "Run the foreigner out," shouted another. "Kill him!" clamored a few hot heads. "Burn Anjiro's house and clean out the whole nest," proposed some other charitable soul. Suggestions now came thick and fast. Only one man seemed to remain calm under the magic influence of the exciting idea that had been tossed into the midst of the inflammable group. It was old Yamanaka. He sat stock-still, biding his time.

When the din had subsided a little, Mr. Yamanaka stood up. When he raised his arm to indicate that he wanted to speak, a measure of silence was soon restored. "Honorable Elders," he began with his usual dignity, "we are listening to a good suggestion. I also thank Mr. Sato for adding this knowledge." He bowed to the old man who had started the hullabaloo. "Only I beg to remark one thing. It is not certain that this is the cause of the fish going away." Shouts of disapproval greeted the doubter, but the old man waved down the interrupters and kept on. "I know the Anjiro family very well," he continued. "Old Anjiro is a good man — honest, and never troubling people. I do not know about his son, nor the foreigner. But instead of burning his house down and killing people, let us get this young man here and inquire about the matter. Is it not better to go slowly? If we then decide this is the reason, it will be time enough to burn and kill people. Am I not speaking true doctrine?"

This appealed to the older men at once, and the younger bloods cooled down when they saw the way the wind was blowing. One of them was sent off forthwith to find young Anjiro and bring him to the meeting. Time was not valuable when there was no fishing to do, and the assembled delegates found no trouble in passing an hour's wait in their accustomed occupation of making endless comments to each other on the trivialities of life in a fishing village. This long wait also gave them plenty of time to cool their first ardor for violent and instantaneous action.

When Paul Anjiro walked into the meeting, he was not without some trepidation, but he was determined not to show it. He could feel the hostility that told him he was on thin ice, but he believed in facing things. The first Christian of Japan was a young man of boldness. Besides, he had a supreme confidence in the man who had made him a Christian. "If I get into any trouble here," he consoled himself, "Father Xavier will know how to get me out." This was not as certain as he imagined; for Father Xavier, as the first foreigner in Japan, was certain to meet with much opposition himself. But Paul was confident.

Without disclosing their suspicions, the old men questioned Paul very closely about his own movements and particularly about the foreigner lodging in his house. When did he come? Why had he come? What sort of man was he? What business was he engaged in? Paul's answers opened their eyes. So the foreigner was a bonze also — a holy man who preached doctrine and exercised virtues. This intelligence allayed the fears of some and increased those of others. A holy man would not do the place any harm, some said. But a bonze of some foreign religion will anger all our deities and bring down their vengeance upon us, argued others. Finally old Mr. Yamanaka brushed through the word-sowing with a question to the point.

"Anjiro," he said, "do you know why we brought you here? I will tell you to hear. Some bad luck has driven away the fish from our bay. This has not happened in the memory of man, and we know there is some evil omen around. Some think this foreign bonze you brought here is the cause of it."

Paul was relieved more than surprised to learn the real trouble. He appeared not the least bit disconcerted. "Mr. Yamanaka," he said calmly, "when did the fish go away?"

"About a month ago. Yes, it's fully a month now, I think," replied Yamanaka, looking around for corrobora-

128

tion. The old graybeards nodded approval. A murmur of assent ran through the assembly. They all had good reason to know. It was fully a month, and it seemed in their gloomy retrospect more like a year.

"Well," said Paul with deliberation, "we arrived here a week ago. Does that look as if we drove the fish away?"

This won the argument. A few die-hards tried to contend that the spirit took account of their coming in advance and got angry three weeks ahead of time, but this was too much for the general credulity. The Elders pronounced against this theory almost unanimously. The old man who had started the trouble was still unsatisfied. "Well," he said gloomily, "maybe they were not the cause of it. I admit it is not certain. But what was? We are now right back where we started. And the question still is: How bring back the fish?"

Paul had a bold thought. "You want to see the fish come back?" he asked calmly, as if ordering fish around was a commonplace in his life. "Suppose I ask Father Xavier to bring them back."

"What! Has he this power?" exclaimed one old man. "Don't believe it. He is more likely to scare them away," shouted others. Another babel ensued. But many thought it was no harm to try, and this opinion carried the day.

"Mind, I am not promising he will do it," explained Paul. "Only I know he has done many wonders much greater than this. I will ask him. I know he will be glad to come and talk with you about it."

On the shore of the bay stood a crowd of fishermen and villagers. They listened avidly to a strange-looking foreigner in a black gown and a white surplice reciting still stranger sounds from a little black book. It was the first time the

Roman Ritual was ever used in Japan. "O God, who dividing the waters from the dry land, hast created every living thing therein, and hast willed that man should command the fishes of the sea; who walking on the swelling depths of the sea didst command the winds and the waves, and by Thy word didst fill the nets of the Apostles; grant, we beseech Thee, that Thy servants, freed from all dangers by Thy protection, may encompass in their boats a copious multitude of fishes. Through Christ Our Lord. Amen."

Father Xavier turned and made a sweeping sign of the cross that included the boats, the people, the whole bay. "Try again tomorrow," he said. "Perhaps God will hear your prayers."

"Well, did they catch any fish?" asked Xavier of Paul, the next day.

"Piles of them. Nets full. And you caught a few also. Old man Yamanaka and his family already want to study the doctrine. And I am sure there will be more to follow."

THE ROAD to KYOTO

IT was four o'clock in the morning of a bitter January day. Most people in the inn were still sound asleep, but there were stirrings and groanings here and there as wakefulness spread among the huddled figures. A few fortunate ones with no place to go opened eyes in the darkness and promptly turned over for another snug session under the blankets. Others were less fortunate. Kyoto-bound travelers tumbled off the board beds with teeth chattering, and began hastily to wrap up their blankets and assemble their piecemeal baggage in the murky flicker of the peanut-oil lamps. Some ran out to hitch the horses, and soon the inn courtyard was full of bustle and stir in spite of the early hour. A sleepy cook was dishing up steaming rice and scalding tea. The encouraging odors permeated the chill air of the bleak compound, and the shivering men sniffed appreciatively as they hobbled about their preparations for departure.

The spryest man in the group was the oldest. Apparently it fell to his lot to issue the orders. He did it with a will, darting here and hopping there, ordering that horse to be harnessed more tightly, this pannier to be tied more securely, and everything to be done more quickly. He did not look important, bundled in the voluminous padded gown that swallowed him up much after the manner of a turtle, and left nothing to be seen but a sharp nose and a pair of bright eyes. Yet the

131

sluggish porters and the surly soldiers all jumped to do his
bidding. It was plain to be seen that his word was law. This
was only partly because he had hired the whole retinue for
the long trip to Kyoto. He was a Daimyo of Japan.

"Ought to have more soldiers, Honorable Sir." The Daimyo turned in surprise to find the head porter bowing respectfully to the ground. "This is the dangerous part. Full
of bandits. The men are afraid."

"Nonsense!" The old man bristled. "Afraid of what? A
few bandits? Why, a dozen soldiers are enough for all the
bandits in Japan!" The Daimyo began stamping around.
"Afraid!" he spluttered. "What is Japan coming to? Now
when I was young, a little danger would make us all the more
determined to go on. The men of this generation are a dis-
grace to their ancestors!"

"Oh, they are willing to go, alright," interposed the
porter hastily. He did not relish a long lecture at that hour
in the morning, especially from a Daimyo who might supple-
ment it with a stroke of the sword. Even when traveling
outside the principality over which he ruled, the Daimyo's
word was law. "They are all saying the guard is too small,
that's all. I just thought I'd tell you."

"It's a nice time to tell me, I must say," grumbled the
Daimyo. "Even if we needed more men, where could I hire
them now? Want me to go and wake up everybody in the
inn? Anyhow, these people are all merchants. They can't
protect us. They want us to protect them."

"Do you mind if we accompany your party?" interrupted
a voice at his elbow. The Daimyo turned around in surprise. He saw a husky young Japanese clad in short jacket
and tucked-up trousers, apparently ready for the road. Back

132

of him stood four strange figures, evidently his companions. In the murky light the Daimyo peered closer. One he saw at once to be a Chinese. The dark-skinned young man next to him appeared to be an Indian. But the other two with the bushy beards and the long black gowns! "What's this?" he ejaculated. "Some kind of bonzes?" He squinted again. "What! They are Europeans! Can't speak our Japanese words probably. What in the world brings them here?"

"Honorable Sir, we are on the way to Kyoto," began one of the odd-looking men in an accent that immediately stamped him a non-Japanese. "We learned you were leaving this morning, so we hurried over. . . ."

"Kyoto! What will you do there?" exclaimed the old man. "Who are you? If I mistake not, you are strangers to our Japanese land."

"We are teachers of religion," said the foreigner gravely. "We are going to Kyoto to see the Mikado."

"To see the Mikado? Indeed!" The Daimyo smiled as if he had just heard an excellent joke. His good humor increased. "Well, my friends, you will be very lucky if you succeed. It's not an easy matter to see the Mikado of Japan." He paused and chuckled, as he recalled the last time he himself had penetrated to that august personage. It had cost him a pretty penny in bribes, and had done him little practical good, as the Mikado was entirely shorn of power and lived more or less a prisoner in his own palace. "And as for teaching religion," he continued, "it's my opinion you will have little better success with that. Why add a new religion to the confusion that exists now? Japan has too many religions already."

"That is what we ourselves think, Honorable Sir. Where

133

many religions exist, there must be confusion. Religion comes from God, and you cannot have two true religions without making Him a liar. We wish to make known in Japan the one true religion, established not by us but by God above."

"Well, maybe so. Can't stop to argue." The Daimyo's memory stirred. He turned to the young Japanese. "Where did you men come from? Sakai? Are you the men my friend Tanaka spoke about yesterday? Said some religious teachers were trying to get to Kyoto. Wanted me to take them along."

The young Japanese traveler stepped forward. "We are the men. We met Tanaka San in Sakai. Our friends in Yamaguchi gave us a letter to him. We left there last week, but we started out two months ago from Kagoshima. That is my inferior place of abode."

"All the way from Kagoshima! You are surely great travelers. It's a wonder to me you got this far alive. Well, come along. Glad you found me. I would have looked for you, but I had many things on my mind." The Daimyo resumed his role of busy traveler. He turned to the porter. "Maybe that will satisfy your men," he said, chuckling. "Tell them we have reinforcements! Five strong men. If the bandits see those beards, they will run the other way. Hurry up now. Get the men together. We must get started." The old man made a little bow to his new recruits and scuttled off to hasten his final preparations for the start.

It did not take long for everybody to gobble down a bowl of rice, and it was still dark when the cavalcade filed out of the courtyard. The Daimyo and his soldiers on their horses took the lead. Then came the merchants, some on horseback and some afoot, while the porters with the baggage strung along at a dog-trot in the rear. No horses had been provided for the five strangers, so they filed along with the porters and servants. The two Europeans tucked up their black gowns and took long strides that enabled them to keep up with the trotting porters. All walked rapidly. The road was packed with snow and it crunched under their feet, making a slippery but hard path, and in the bitter cold the exercise was gratifying. The pace was too fast to encourage conversation; nothing was heard but the labored breathing of the men as they hurried along.

After two hours the hardy porters, long inured to this sort of travel, still kept to their brisk trot. A gray dawn had come up; overcast and forbidding, with a promise of more snow. The two Europeans were puffing and blowing. Occasionally their steps lagged. Their young Japanese companion watched them anxiously. Finally he voiced his fears.

"Are you tired, Father Francis? We do not need to keep up with the party, unless we want to. It may be better to rest."

The European smiled. He turned to his companion. "Maybe Brother Fernandez is tired, Bernard. What do you say, Brother? Are we tired already? And shall we take a rest?"

"So soon?" exclaimed Fernandez. "No, Father, not I. Why, we are just starting. How about taking a rest at Kyoto?" He struck out at a brisker pace. "I can't answer for Emmanuel and Amador," he added. "It's a pretty cold country for them, I'm afraid." He turned to their two other companions. "How about it, boys?"

"The colder it is, the faster we walk," said Amador, the young Indian. "Besides, we go anywhere with Father Fran-

135

cis." Emmanuel, the Chinese, vigorously nodded his head. "Good walking," he remarked. "Also have tea houses by and by." The two southern boys were travelers.

"All right," replied Bernard, somewhat reassured. "Only don't hesitate to say so when you get tired. Even for us Japanese, you know, this is a fast pace. And the trip is long."

They trudged along, mile after mile. Father Francis masked his weariness by forced animation. He took an apple from his pocket, tossed it in the air and caught it, skipping and dancing along. Occasionally he sang out a snatch from a Latin psalm. The porters looked at him curiously, smiling at the strange figure and the stranger words.

Soon they began halting at the tea houses, the whole party resting for five minutes while swallowing cups of scalding tea. The short waits were life-savers to the missioners. But these oases did not last. Part of the road they had chosen was little traveled and had few tea houses. There was no stop for a midday meal, and as the afternoon wore on, a whole three hours passed without a single tea house to stop at. The Daimyo was nervous. He showed it by barking out unnecessary orders. This isolated section was notorious for bandits, and he did not want to lose any time putting it behind him. He kept urging the soldiers and the porters all along the line.

Father Francis was plodding along, lost in meditation, when the first arrow swished past his ear. It struck a basket suspended on the carrying-pole of a porter, embedding itself with a heavy thud. Father Francis looked up to see the load of baggage strewn on the roadway, as the porter spun around and fell sprawling. He ran to help the fallen man, but the porter had scrambled off the road and found cover behind the roadside dike before he could reach him. More arrows

136

flew past but they found no target. The long column of soldiers and porters had vanished like magic. Father Francis
looked around. Except for himself and Brother Fernandez,
everybody had melted into the paddy field, leaving the road
empty.

"Take them in the rear! Put over a volley! What kind of
soldiers are you? Ito, push over on the left with your column.
You take the right, Ikeda, and hurry up. Go right in and surround them. They are in that clump of trees over there."
The shouting and gesticulating Daimyo was still on his horse,
now prancing around in the rice stubble. His men were flat
on their faces behind the dike. Another shower of arrows
came over. Yet no bowmen were seen approaching. The
Daimyo stopped his horse. Suddenly he was icy calm. He
held up his hand.

"Center, stand up and deliver. Right and left, charge."
At the sound of the Daimyo's voice the whole line of soldiers
sprang into action. The end columns had already broken
across the road when the center group let go with their arrows. They sent volley after volley into the distant grove, as
the right and left wings converged on their objective.

The Daimyo spurred his horse up on the road to join Father
Francis and Brother Fernandez. He jumped off his horse.
He looked bored. "They will not find anybody there," the
Daimyo announced to the two wondering foreigners. "The
affair is over. No real fighting in this country any more. All
they do is count heads, and then the side that is outnumbered
runs away. I could tell from their first volley that they were
not many. It's just their way of finding out if we were prepared to fight. You notice they kept a line of retreat open.

137

They will be scattered back in that woods somewhere before our soldiers get there."

The Daimyo proved to be a good prophet. No more arrows came from the edge of the forest. The soldiers stopped shooting as their charging companions reached the grove and plunged into it from both sides. The porters climbed back on the road from the rice field. Looking a little sheepish, the missioners' three companions, Bernard, Emmanuel and Amador, picked themselves up and came toward them. The Daimyo was watching the spot where the soldiers had disappeared in the woods. He saw a group emerging. He relaxed and smiled.

"I thought so," said the Daimyo, turning to the missioners. "Small group of bandits. Already ran away. Probably won't catch a single one of them. Can't stop to round them up. I've got to get to Kyoto. As soon as the soldiers get in line, we'll start moving." The old man came closer to Father Francis and peered into his face with his sharp little eyes. His manner was friendly. "You and your friend are brave men," he said. "You stood your ground. That helped to keep our men together. These bandits always try to stampede people by a sudden attack and scatter them. Then they chase the small groups and rob them." He paused, not quite satisfied with his little speech. "I am glad you came with us," he added. "The worst is now over. Soon we shall be in Kyoto." He jumped on his horse and hastened to the head of the forming column.

It was a weary cavalcade that finally stumbled into the streets of the Capital late that evening. It was too dark to see anything. Bernard chose the first inn they came to. The missioners collapsed immediately upon their board beds. The three boys busied themselves getting hot water. Brother Fernandez washed his feet in the scalding water. He felt better immediately. But when Father Francis took off his worn shoes, his feet were cracked with chilblains and bleeding. They all tried to down a little of the rice and tea that were provided, but they were too tired to eat. Father Francis brightened for a moment. "Bernard!" he exclaimed. "God bless your perseverance. And Amador and Emmanuel! Well done! We are in Kyoto! Tomorrow we will try to see the Emperor! But what we all need now is a good night's sleep."

The man at the gate did not look much like the attendant of an Emperor. He was dressed like an ordinary soldier. Neither did he seem to feel that the group confronting him looked like visitors to an Emperor. He surveyed the strange figures with distaste. "You want to see the Mikado?" he barked, scowling and staring. "Who are you? And what business brings you here? Have you got a letter from the Shogun? Let me see the presents you are bringing."

The visitors stood perplexed. Presents! Letter from the Shogun! And here they were — empty-handed. Of a truth, they were not prepossessing in appearance. A night's sleep had lessened their fatigue, but their clothes were in tatters. The two missioners looked outlandish with their ragged black cassocks, worn-out shoes and flopping Siamese hats. Their heavy beards added to the strangeness. They could have qualified as scarecrows. The Tamil boy was dressed in his simple native coolie clothes. Emmanuel, the Chinese, had donned the long gown that denotes a scholar, but the garment was so faded and patched after long use and hard travel that its wearer would have been more easily taken for a strolling musician or a medicine seller. Only Bernard showed some semblance of respectability. The young Japanese had carefully carried a new winter kimono all the way from Kagoshima for such occasions. He listened calmly to the rude greeting. He bowed and resumed his role of spokesman.

"Good friend, this inferior person told you to hear that we have an important message for the Mikado bearing on religion. A very important message. We have come from Kagoshima to deliver it. In fact, these two religious teachers have come all the way from Europe with no other purpose. And these young men have journeyed from India. May we implore your superior instructions as to our procedure in making our obeisance to His Majesty?" The young Japanese concluded his speech with another bow. He tried to look a hopefulness he did not feel.

The gate keeper never changed his scowl. He listened with fidgeting impatience. He turned his back on the visitors and addressed his two assistants. "These men do not know any customs," he said. "Have the excessive effrontery to come here and ask to see the Mikado." He turned back to his questioners. "I told you to hear that what you ask is impossible. The Mikado does not see strangers. No use to talk. I cannot let you in. It is not the custom. I am busy." He turned away, then suddenly halted and gave them a sidewise glance. His manner changed. His voice lowered. "A man was admitted to the inner courtyard last week. He brought ten gold bars and a bushel of peacock feathers. I do not know if he saw the Mikado. These affairs have nothing to do with me."

Father Francis began a speech. The man looked at him a moment contemptuously. "No use to talk," he interrupted bluntly, and walked away.

The visitors hesitated, looking from one to the other. Bernard whispered in Father Francis' ear. The priest nodded. The interview was over. The five travelers left the palace gate and started on their way. If they were to see the Emperor Go-Nara, it would have to be some other day. They picked their way slowly back to the inn.

Father Francis was not a man to give up his design quickly, but neither was he a man who learned slowly. It did not take him long to obtain a good light on the situation in Kyoto, nor did the growing impatience of his companions escape him while he was doing it. When Brother Fernandez finally came to him with a complaint about wasting time, he was ready. He called his little group together.

"We have been here eleven days," began Father Francis, "and we have not seen the Mikado. We have preached in the streets with no success. We have no place to stay but this inn — and very little money. It is time to go back."

The men were silent. Bernard stirred uneasily. Suddenly he spoke. "I am sorry, Father. I did not know the customs in this place. Our trip has been a failure."

"Nothing is a failure that is done for God, Bernard," replied Father Francis quickly. "We came here to find out what He wants us to do — maybe to see the Mikado, maybe not. This trip has its own success. We know a great deal more now than we knew before. The Mikado leads a retired life. If he abstains from the state affairs of the country, he is not likely to take any active interest in us. We must look elsewhere. And there are no universities here. All these big

141

establishments are nothing but Buddhist monasteries. All this we learned. Isn't that something?"

Bernard was relieved. "Yes, Father," he chimed in. "And we learned that nothing is done here without presents and money. I should have known that about Kyoto. Caused you to lose a lot of face."

"My face can stand it," rejoined the missioner. "And don't worry about Kyoto. It will have its day in God's plan. Now let's go back to Yamaguchi and learn some more about how to convert Japan."

IDEWALK PITCH

THERE was a sharp rap on the sliding panel that served for a door, and the two missioners looked up from their struggles over Japanese hieroglyphics to exchange a rapid glance of interrogation. Thoughts of ubiquitous soldiers flashed through the minds of men who had been prepared by three months in Japan to be surprised at everything. It was almost with a sense of disappointment that the younger man slid back the panel to reveal the smiling face of Francis Xavier.

"Oh, it's you, Father." There was, however, more relief than disappointment in his tone. No cohorts of the Shogun this time, and here was the head man of the outfit to deal with them when they did come. The week of Xavier's absence had seemed long.

"Of course, it's I," laughed Xavier, as he shook hands. "Who else would it be to seek out our little mission? You haven't got the crowds coming already, have you?" He strode around, beaming on both his companions. He was evidently delighted to get back. Suddenly he wheeled about. "But we shall have them coming soon! Look here!" He bent over his knapsack and extracted a small notebook. He threw it on the table.

"What's that?" asked one of the mystified men. "Is that all you brought back?"

"All? My dear man, isn't that enough?" replied Xavier,

with a twinkling eye. "Behold, Father Torres, the key to Japan!"

"Humph," commented Torres, unimpressed. "Funny-looking key. Of course, I admit that Japan is also a pretty funny lock. What is it going to open, and how?"

"Why, the hearts of the people, Father, what else? Do you know what that little book is? It is the entire résumé of Christian Doctrine translated into good Japanese by Bernard and Paul at Kagoshima. They already had the rough part done, and we worked the entire week to polish it up. Do you say it was time well spent? Juan Fernandez, what do you think?"

The other man jumped up eagerly. He seized the book and began to thumb it over. "Time well spent?" he breathed. "Indeed it was better spent than the week we passed here in trying to learn a few sounds by word of mouth. Good heavens, what a language! I was beginning to think there was no way to learn it at all. Now this is what I call a real step." He sat down again, still leafing here and there in the precious book. He tried to pronounce a few of the new words under his breath. Father Torres joined him to have a peep.

Xavier was studying the pair fondly. "Ah, you are both young and will make short work of it. That's right; dig into it. It won't be long before we can sally out and do some real work."

Fernandez looked up jubilantly. "Father, this is just the thing. All the Christian terms! Why, as soon as we have learned this, we shall be ready to get out and preach."

"Well, I should hope so," replied Father Francis. "That's what we came here for. And that's why we put in all the work on this little book." He paused, sighed. Mission work always seemed to take such a long way around to get any-where. And there was so much work to do. It was hard not to be able to pitch in at once. "But we must hurry, Juan. Think of it! Three months in Japan already, and no way to tell the people what brought us here!"

Fernandez was still thumbing the new book. "Give me a week at this, Father Francis, and I'll take a chance at preach-ing a sermon. I think I have already seized the hang of the sentence structure more or less. And I know a lot of the ordinary words. As soon as I get these religious terms, I'm your man."

The week went by amid hectic study and redoubled prayers. Brother Juan Fernandez was a natural linguist, and he made much more rapid progress in the difficult language than the other two. He was a little abashed, but also elated, when Father Xavier selected him to make the first attempt at preaching to the people.

For his pitch Xavier had picked out the corner of a street near a much-frequented temple, because he had noticed that there was usually a lot of coming and going at this point. His foresight was not entirely necessary, as the pair of foreigners would have gathered a crowd anywhere. In fact, they auto-matically collected one as they went along, and, by the time they had arrived at the chosen spot, they were already the center of a curious throng. Small boys danced around them, laughing and making faces; young men stared pop-eyed, and old men raised eyebrows in mild and benevolent curiosity. Even some of the women took furtive peeps at the extraordi-nary strangers, although they quickly lowered their eyes again to the pavement, and proceeded to look quite incapable of even so momentary a breach of Oriental customs.

The temple steps were already crowded with worshipers. Xavier glanced about and concluded that a voice raised in this vicinity would be heard by upwards of a hundred people. He gave the signal to Fernandez. "We'll say the 'Our Father' together for a start," he said. "Then launch right out."

The prayer arrested the attention of the curious mob, and a measure of comparative quiet pervaded the chattering groups. This gave Fernandez a good opening. He shouted out the carefully conned sentences of his introduction. With his great gift for languages he was already able to reproduce the native pronunciation to a fair extent; and, rather to his own surprise, he at once found himself speaking to an attentive audience.

"Good heavens, they actually understand me," was the welcome thought he framed unconsciously, as he continued to pour out words. His ready memory and facile tongue warmed to their work, and he was soon preaching a very fair sermon in a Japanese that, while far from perfect, was yet intelligible. The audience tittered now and again at some mispronunciation or inversion of word order, but the gist of the speech was being understood sufficiently to rivet attention.

But it was not to be all plain sailing. Catcalls and shrill laughter came from the youngsters, who would not have understood, in any language, the subjects the preacher was discussing. Occasionally a shout of derision arose. Fernandez explained the unity of God and the futility of honoring a multiplicity of idols. This provoked a few jeers, but no serious opposition, as most of the listeners were themselves

146

inclined to regard the idols they worshiped as beings of rather vague and questionable powers. Besides, Fernandez kept the discussion at first on a speculative basis. But soon it came time for brass tacks.

When he had clarified the question sufficiently, he began to insinuate its practical bearing. He did so by explaining the reason that had brought the missioners to Japan. "It is to bring you this message that we have come to your honor-able country. It is not your own fault that you do not know the one true God. How could you know, if nobody told you? So our presence in Japan is in order to teach you. . . ."

Brother Fernandez stopped. There was a commotion on the edge of the crowd; and, as he looked about for the source of the interruption, he saw a middle-aged man elbowing his way through the press, shouting and sputtering as he came. Neither Fernandez nor Xavier could make out what the man was saying, but from his violent gesticulations it was obvious that he was working himself into a towering rage. "Give him a chance," whispered Francis to Fernandez. "This may add to the attraction."

The vigorous objector had now penetrated through the throng. He planted himself directly in front of Fernandez. Indignation oozed from his kimono-clad figure. Fernandez smiled at him ingratiatingly, but he was in no mood to be placated by smiles. He looked straight at the missioner, and there was no favor in his glance.

"Teach us!" he howled. "Did you say you came to Japan to teach us?" The scorn of an insulted continent was in his tones. "Beggarly foreign devils! Who invited *you* to come and teach us, I'd like to know?" He turned to the crowd. "These wonderful scholars came to teach us," he shouted in derision. "Of course, we don't know anything in Japan, so we need these scarecrow foreigners to come and teach us!"

The irate heckler paused to collect a supply of breath for a further onslaught, and Brother Fernandez got his chance to pour some oil on the waters. He smiled again, adopted his mildest tone, and took special care with his inflections. "Honorable Sir," he began, "you mistake my meaning. We came to Japan to learn as well as to teach. In many departments of knowledge your esteemed country is no doubt superior to our wretched fatherland." A murmur of approval went up from the crowd at this compliment. "But I am confining myself simply to one subject, and . . ."

"What is it? What is the subject you are going to teach us then?" interrupted his truculent interlocutor.

Fernandez wanted this question, and he let his adversary have the answer full and fair. "Religion," he said. "We are priests of God. There is only One. There is no other — whether in Japan, or any place else. And consequently all these idols. . . ."

His opponent snapped him up again. "What's the matter with our idols? We have had them for hundreds of years! And you say they are no good? Who are *you*, anyway? Why don't you stay in your own country?"

"We are sent. And sent, not by men, but by Almighty God, in order to explain His doctrine. You are free, of course, not to listen. Nobody is forcing you. But how can you learn about God unless somebody teaches you?"

The speech was too incisive for the angry man. It left him a bit bewildered, and it ended on a note that had already galled him to the quick. He lost control of himself.

"Teach us! There it is again! This rascally foreigner

148

keeps on talking about teaching us!" he shrieked, half turning to the crowd as he edged up to Fernandez. "Well, we'll do a little teaching, too. And I'll give you your first lesson right now, you foreign busybody," he ended. And with the words the enraged man spat full in Fernandez' face.

Xavier was watching closely. A little stir of sympathy rippled along the sea of faces as Fernandez paled, stood stock-still a moment, then flushed deeply and involuntarily raised his arm.

Just for what purpose he raised his arm only he himself ever knew. Xavier's whisper was instant in his ear. "The other cheek, Juan. We preach Christ crucified."

The preacher's arm described a graceful circle and then fell to the pocket of his soutane, from which he drew a handkerchief. In a leisurely fashion he wiped his face, smiling once more. He saw his adversary already moving off. Apparently much of his feeling was spent, though he still muttered and gesticulated. Fernandez smiled at the crowd. "As I was saying," he resumed serenely, "there is only one true God."

Fernandez and Xavier were leaving the square, when a dignified looking man of the merchant type accosted them with a low bow. "Honorable Sirs, may I have the privilege of a word with you?" he inquired.

The two missioners stopped at once. "Certainly, Sir," replied Xavier, returning the bow. "Can we be of any service to your honorable personality?"

"You are men of religion," said the merchant. "I am only a merchant, yet I am also a humble aspirant to virtue. All my life I am seeking it. But it is hard to find. In fact, I was beginning to think there was no such thing, until this morning. In my fifty years of mortal life, I have never before seen an example of true virtue such as my eyes witnessed just now." He turned and bowed low to Brother Fernandez. "You, Sir, have some secret of virtue superior to us ordinary men. Otherwise, how could you calmly smile at such an affront?"

Fernandez returned the bow. "This base person is unworthy of these good words. This is not the strength of weak men such as ourselves, but the power of God above. He is helping us. He will help you. He makes virtue easy. That is the secret."

"I confess, Honorable Sir," returned the merchant, "that this insignificant man has never found virtue easy. Indeed, a long life has taught me to look upon it as unattainable. But you evidently have some means of reaching it. I am desiring to hear more about this doctrine."

"Where is your precious residence?" put in Xavier.

"Here is the address of my snailshell hovel," said the merchant, producing his card. "May I have the honor to welcome your jade footsteps?"

"At the first opportunity we shall pay our respects," promised Father Xavier.

"Well, Juan," said Francis Xavier, as the two started to retrace their steps to their temporary mission, "perhaps your Japanese wasn't perfect. But when you turned the other cheek, you spoke a language that was understood. It was the best sermon you ever preached."

THE TROUBADOUR

PREACHING in the streets of Yamaguchi was a hard-enough task under the best conditions, in the opinion of good Brother Fernandez, and he was not disposed to welcome any extra hazards that made it harder. They had weathered the first outbursts of catcalling and derision. They had persevered through the ensuing period of stony indifference. They had smiled their way into the good graces of the street urchins, who now greeted them and joked with them instead of pelting them with mud. And now, just as they had reached the point where the crowds were beginning to give them a fairly respectful hearing, this poor blind minstrel had to come sidling along with his caterwauling music that made such a distracting din. And that was only part of it. The clowning pantomimes he went through in the course of his performance made an even greater distraction. Brother Fernandez lost the thread of his own discourse several times just in watching the man. And the interminable ballads and ditties that he sang in his quavering, falsetto voice! One might as well try to preach in the middle of a street fair. Why did the good man need to pick the very same time and place to rehearse his show, when he had the whole town open to him all day long?

Brother Fernandez suddenly checked himself. Was he becoming impatient? After all, the streets were free to anybody. And the sightless man had a living to make. It was just one of those awkward complications, that was all. Brother Fernandez sidled over to the blind singer. He quietly slipped some coins in his little bowl. He hastened down the street to join Father Xavier and the others, who had taken their leave of the little listening crowd, and started home. He whispered a prayer for the blind man as he went. He sighed and decided to think of something else.

The missioners were not discouraged with their work in Yamaguchi. They had made a little solid progress, in spite of the very rude reception accorded them at the beginning. They were now known and tolerated in the place and had even managed to make a few sincere converts. Signs of interest were not lacking. But they were not getting any appreciable results with their street preaching, and apart from their casual contacts with individuals, this was their only method. They knew that Yamaguchi was one of the most important cities in Japan, and they had a feeling that the field was a fertile one, if only they possessed the means to cultivate it. They had the permission of the Daimyo, obtained after a lot of trouble, to preach and baptize. They had even been given an old abandoned Buddhist monastery to live in. Their strange abode brought them a lot of curious visitors. Their situation was not bad. It was so good that it made them wonder why their progress was not greater.

The blind man was getting to be a fixture at their street meetings. Even when they changed their pitch to test the effect of their preaching in other parts of the city, it would not be long before the tinkle of the koto announced the advent of their rival. The minstrel man did not always interrupt their preaching. Sometimes he kept quiet. Perhaps he even listened. Once he surprised Brother Fernandez by ask-

152

ing a question. Why was it that some men were good and others bad, he wanted to know. Fernandez answered it to the best of his ability. But the very next minute the blind man struck the chords of his big, unwieldy dulcimer and went into a burst of wailing song. Was he crazy? Brother Fernandez did not know. He thought it might be worth mentioning to Father Xavier.

Father Xavier did not seem surprised when he heard the question. He liked to talk about the mission work in the momentary leisure of their evening recreation. He smiled. "That thought came to me, Brother," he said. "It is curious how this poor, blind singer has followed us around. But I don't think he is crazy. Maybe God sent him. You know, that is always a possibility. Especially when you are engaged in this kind of work that advances His kingdom." Father Xavier smiled again. He suddenly put his arm around the other man's shoulder and gave him a little pat. "Brother, you are a good preacher. And I am a poor one. But we are a pair of foreigners in Japan, and both of us together are not the equal of this old blind man. How eloquent he is in his own fashion. I know he is not helping us much with this continual din he is making. But I am beginning to think he is a born catechist. What's the matter with our work here? Above all, we need some native helpers. Have you thought of that? Bernard is a good boy, but he is too young to impress these people. I doubt if this old man is trying to interfere with us. A blind man has to follow crowds to make a living. He may even be interested. He asked you a question the other day. Let's be patient with the old fellow and see what happens."

A dim peanut-oil lamp flickered long that night in the old

Buddhist monastery, as Brother Fernandez pored over his few Japanese books in putting together a new sermon. He wanted to tell a story that he knew very well, but he was obliged to hunt up a lot of new Japanese words to express it. He kept Bernard up a long time to help him correct his effort. He worked very late. As he tumbled into bed he said a final prayer that his new sermon might be successful.

There was only the nucleus of a crowd as the missioners started their usual program the next morning. But Brother Fernandez had not proceeded very far in his routine outline of the elements of the Faith when he saw the old minstrel come tapping his way along. As soon as the old man felt his way to the wall of the corner house, he squatted down with the big koto and began his strumming. Before he could begin to sing, Brother Fernandez launched into his newly prepared sermon.

The crowd seemed unusually small this morning. "Only a few curiosity seekers," thought Fernandez. "And not even very many of them." Then he was into his story and forgot his audience. He found his prepared phrases coming pat, and he got interested in the story himself. He told of a Great Teacher who once walked the roads of Palestine, scattering His blessings broadcast out of compassion for the multitude. He related how He and His companions were one day drawing nigh to Jericho when a blind man by the wayside asked what was happening, and was told that Jesus of Nazareth was passing by. He described the appeal of the blind man for help, and how the crowd rebuked him and bade him be still, only to have him cry out the more until his plea was heard; and how the Great Teacher stood still and looked upon him, and loved him, and read his heart, and asked him what he willed. "Lord, that I may see." And then he told how the

154

divine answer came in response to that sincere and trusting prayer: "Receive thy sight; thy faith hath made thee whole."

The strumming dulcimer was still and no sound came from the listening crowd. Brother Fernandez ended his story and went on to conclude his sermon with his usual peroration about the happiness of heaven and the eternal evil of hell. He noticed that the crowd had swelled to fair proportions. But what made them all so quiet? Nobody asked a question; nobody approached him; nobody stirred. Was it another failure to reach their hearts — just more seed sown by the wayside? Well, who could tell? He watched the bystanders as they began drifting away.

Suddenly he heard the strains of the koto, and his eyes turned to the street corner where the old minstrel had ensconced himself. Was that Father Francis — dancing in the streets of Japan! Even that could not surprise Brother Fernandez, for he had seen Xavier dancing along the road to Kyoto when there had been less to be jubilant about. As he strolled over, Father Francis halted the little step he was executing and the strumming stopped.

"Just a little celebration, Brother," he heard Xavier saying to him. "Our friend thinks we could combine our show and work together. He wants to learn the doctrine. And perhaps some day we can learn to play the koto. I told him that we could not cure his eyes, mind you, but he is not worried about that. He has been listening to the doctrine all the time. And he says his soul can see."

The missioners had found their catechist. The sightless eyes had seen and the old ballad-singer had a new vocation. For in him they found the man who would be known as Brother Lawrence, the blind apostle of Yamaguchi, the first Jesuit vocation in Japan.

# FAITH ENTERS in SILK

FUNAI had never seen anything like it. The two small boats in front served as an escort. The Portuguese sailors who manned them were dressed in their best. In the bow of each boat stood a man blowing shrill fanfares on a silver trumpet, as if to announce the approach of something or somebody extraordinary. Not far behind them came the big shallop. It was decked out from stem to stern. Silken banners streamed in the wind from every corner of it. Pennants encircled it. Over the water came the sound of lively music from the pipers and drum, mers ranged on its deck. Down the streets and alleys of Funai people came running to the waterfront. By the time the boats drew alongside the praya a great crowd had gath, ered. They jostled and pushed in their efforts to see the dele, gation the foreign ships were bringing.

Captain da Gama was in the lead. In his full dress uniform and with his head held high, he looked every inch a Com, mander. He strode up the stone steps, turned sharply and barked out an order to his men. As quickly as the sailors stepped ashore, they lined up in precise formation. Captain da Gama turned and bowed profoundly as the next passen, ger disembarked. He was evidently the guest of honor. "At your orders, Father Xavier," said the Captain. Could the distinguished visitor be Father Francis? He was a foreign priest, yet he did not present the shabby appearance that had come to be the hallmark of the missioner. He was dressed in a brand-new silk cassock and a white lace surplice. Over that he wore a rich looking green-velvet stole. To the bystanders these garments were strange but impressive. More impressive still were the signs of deference with which the Portuguese manifestly regarded him. The sailors stood at attention. The Captain helped him ceremoniously up the steps. Next came the ship's officers, trailing the priest respectfully as if they were his servants. The crowd watched intently.

The procession formed to march to the Daimyo's palace. The sailors marched ahead in double file. Each one was carrying some object that piqued still further the curiosity of the bystanders. The first pair carried two big banners. Others bore articles of a mixed variety taken from the ship. One carried the big missal reposing against his chest. Two men had brass candlesticks. One held the ship's bell, another the ship's clock. The ship's cook struggled along with the shiny, big metal mixer used for kneading the dough. Those who had nothing else flaunted pennants taken from the shallop. The priest carried nothing as he walked sedately along with his hands joined, while the Captain walked at his side as if to assist him. The ship's officers followed, bearing the gifts for the Daimyo. The first one in line bore before him a specially prepared copy of the catechism in Japanese, small in size but sumptuously bound in white satin. The others in turn carried an ornate pair of black-velvet slippers, a gold-headed cane, and a silk parasol. The last officer in line held the most prized gift — a large painting of the Madonna and Child, wrapped in purple damask and borne on a velvet cushion.

157

The procession took the whole town with it as it wended its way along the main streets of the little city. Business seemed almost totally suspended as customers deserted the big market and the street stalls to join the gaping crowd. Old grandmothers herded small children before them, hobbling about on their wooden clogs in search of points of vantage where the little ones could see. Some men held babies on their shoulders. Small boys skipped, scrambled, shrieked, whistled, darted in and out, before and behind. Captain da Gama turned to the missioner. "I think we have them coming our way, Father Francis," he said smilingly. "Poverty is all right for Christian people. But you know, these Orientals like a little show."

Father Francis permitted himself a smile also. "We found that out in Kyoto, Captain. I must say this is a better reception than we ever got there. And we have you to thank for it. God will surely bless you for your help in bringing the true Faith to Funai."

The missioner had his own thoughts as the parade filed slowly along. His mind was working as he surveyed the thronging crowd. The faces turned toward him varied in expression from a respectful composure to eager curiosity and pleased smiles. The parade was an excellent idea. They were providing a little cheer to vary the dull monotony of daily life in Funai, at any rate. He saw none of the hostile masks and stony stares he had learned to expect as a matter of course. "These people have more love of ceremony than love of poverty," he reflected. "After all, they are not Christians yet. We must take them on the flank left open to us. God's Providence is in these things. A religious man must always have poverty. But a missioner is all things to all men. He must use every good means to win the confidence of the people."

Father Francis felt suddenly happy in the new role that he had been so slow to adopt. He knew what a far cry it was from this simple curiosity to serious interest in religion, but nevertheless a good first-impression was not to be despised. He was happy because this revelation of the reactions of the people made him feel he knew them better. His heart warmed to them. He glanced again at the sea of faces that looked out from the swarming crowd. He saw among them the rich and the poor, the young and the old. There were dignified old men and bent old women, shopkeepers and soldiers, peddlers and porters, housewives and young girls, squirming small boys and babes in arms. It was a moving spectacle. "Delight of my soul," came to his lips spontaneously. "What would I not give to see you belong to God."

The young Daimyo of Bungo had left word to usher Father Francis and the officers into his audience hall in the most ceremonious manner. They left the sailor escort in the palace yard. They were led into a seemingly endless series of rooms where they were greeted by various groups of the nobility, partook of refreshments and listened to a long and flowery speech of welcome. Finally they reached the audience hall where the Daimyo was waiting for them. As soon as Father Francis entered the room, the Daimyo left his chair and hastened forward to greet him. He held out both arms to deprecate the need of receiving any obeisance from his guest. Father Francis looked on the courteous young ruler and warmed to him. Whatever the reason, cordiality was evidently the order of the day.

Each officer made a deep bow to Father Francis as he

passed over the gift he was carrying. Father Francis took the gifts and presented each one in turn to the Daimyo. The young man bowed his thanks. When it came to the last gift, Father Francis drew aside the rich purple cloth and disclosed the picture of the Blessed Mother, with her Divine Child. The Daimyo looked surprised. He studied the picture a moment while murmuring his polite phrase of thanks. Evidently it had no meaning for him. So it called for some explanation, as Father Francis had foreseen. The missioner seized his opportunity to give it. In simple, precise phrases he recited the world's most gladsome story.

He told of a night in Bethlehem long ago when God found in the Virgin Mary a human creature worthy to be the tabernacle of His Divine Son and so rent the heavens, in the fullness of His plans, and came down to dwell among us. He told how poor she was, and how she wrapped her Child in swaddling clothes and laid Him in a rude manger, and how the simple shepherds left their flocks in the night and came to greet Him, invited by the angel song. And then he told how the Child grew up and entered upon His mission, and how He went about doing good, preaching to the poor and contrite of heart, raising the dead and healing the sick, calling His apostles and publishing His doctrines — and how He died on the Cross for the sins of all the people and directed that His grace and truth be announced to all men.

The Daimyo listened attentively. His eyes widened. He was visibly impressed. He turned again to the picture and looked at it long and earnestly. He seemed to be reflecting. He stared at the Child of heavenly birth as if he would read some riddle. He studied the gracious, rapt face of the Virgin Mother. Did some ray of light enter his soul as he contem-

160

plated the Divine Child? Or did that Rose of all the world, who held the Infant God in her arms, speak in some fashion to this man who had heard about her Son just now for the first time? He gave no sign. He replaced the picture and turned to Father Francis. He bowed gravely. "This is good doctrine," he said. "Undoubtedly the teachers of this religion are helping men to do good and avoid evil. But in Japan we have our own religions. I have brought some religious teachers here to talk with you about these matters. I will call them in."

The missioner was expecting that a discussion with the Buddhist bonzes might develop. He stood up and watched them file in and kowtow to the Daimyo. When they had ranged themselves against the wall, one bonze stepped forward from the large group and bowed to the assembly. He began a harangue. It had very little to do with religion as such. It was about the propriety of a foreigner presuming to teach a foreign religion in Japan. It ended with the statement that the Japanese possessed the true doctrine and considered it an insult to have another religion brought in from outside.

Father Francis listened calmly. He waited until the orator had come to the end of his long speech. Then he addressed him. "May I ask a question?" he inquired. "If religious doctrine from outside is an insult to the nation, why did you get your own religion from China?"

The bonze was taken aback. He only stared because he could not find an answer. No use denying that the Buddhist teaching came from China when the whole of Japan prided itself on that very fact. Getting no answer, Father Francis went on to comment on the other points of the speech. He chopped into them with University of Paris logic. The bonze looked his annoyance and scorn. He had never before been held to such rigorous responsibility for his statements. Lack-ing all precision of thought and expression, his method of persuasion was the appeal to custom and prejudice, well sprinkled with sarcasm and abuse. He did not know how to defend himself. He had to fall back on staring and sniffing.

"My religion teaches that there is one true God," con-cluded the missioner in the same mild tones with which he had dissected the prejudices of the bonze, "and that He re-vealed one true doctrine to save all men. He loves the Japa-nese people very much, and He does not want them to be excluded from it. That is why I have come here to explain it."

The Daimyo nodded to his attendant and rose from his chair. It was the signal to end the visit. The bonzes filed out. Father Xavier and the Portuguese officers rose and faced their host. All made a deep ceremonious bow together. As he turned to depart, the missioner was surprised to find the Daimyo walking beside him. He accompanied Father Xavier all the way to the palace entrance, a mark of unusual honor. He addressed a final word to the Captain and the officers. "The Father has full approval to preach the doctrine of his religion everywhere in the domain of Bungo," he said. "I want our people to hear it." He bowed and left them.

Father Francis walked back to the shallop with Captain da Gamma. "We made a good entrance in this place, Cap-tain," he said, "and God did the rest. I have Him to thank for a good mission success, and you for a good mission method."

162

THE MESSENGER SAILS

IT was a good plan, and Xavier was so sure of its feasibility that he knelt down and wrote a letter to Ignatius about it. The vast design of the project, with its stake a whole new world of souls, was naturally congenial to the man who had been sent to set the East on fire, and it would find an approving echo in the heart of the man who sent him. It had taken some planning. But the tall, tattered bundle of energy from the hills of Navarre — surveyor of continents, village wayfarer, and university professor all in one — had been painstaking in weighing the chances and tying up the loose ends of the plan, and he thought it was good.

China was the key. The great, sprawling, inaccessible land of storied mystery was to be opened by frontal assault, and if success marked the introduction of the Faith among its teeming millions, the whole Far East would feel the impact from Siam to Japan and the islands of the sea. Every people seemed to have borrowed from China, as from some great reservoir of culture and arts and ethics that overflowed its boundaries and spread to all around; and as every nation owed something to China, so every nation looked to China as a spiritual home. He was tired of hearing the constant question: If your religion is so good, how is it that China does not believe it or even know about it? He would provide the answer to that question. He would go to China and plant the Faith there, so that it might radiate around that immense orbit of the Pacific the more rapidly and claim the very ends of the earth for Christ.

It was not easy to go to China. All travelers and traders were barred from entry, and the few who violated the prohibition were forced to pay for it by long years in gruesome Chinese dungeons. Some even got their heads cut off. Only an official embassy from the Portuguese Crown could hope to secure permission to enter, and there was no Ambassador. To Father Francis the way was plain. It was to create an Ambassador and an embassy on the spot.

It was not the work of a day, nor even of a month, to organize an embassy, but at last everything fell into place. Diego Pereira was a dignified, good man who would make a passable Ambassador. The rich old trader had a ship of his own and money to venture in any profitable enterprise. He could be counted on to bear the expense. As for the rest of the embassy, there was Father Gago and himself, and if they did not suffice, some of the ship's officers could double in the diplomatic role as occasion demanded. Alvaro, the Portuguese lay-brother, would also help. And there was Anthony, the Chinese convert, and Christopher, the Tamil boy, to fill out the party. The court of China had doubtless seen worse retinues than that.

The official appointment of the Ambassador had not been easily forthcoming, but it was fortunate that the Governor of Goa had the power to authorize it. What a delicate piece of work to persuade him! But he finally consented and delivered the documents accrediting Pereira under his hand and seal. If he had some doubts and hesitations, the willingness of the old merchant to pay the expenses of the entire expedition largely removed them. Xavier had seen worse governors. He must remember to pray for the good man every day.

Even the sea was smiling. He could not remember a smoother passage than this past fortnight on the *Santa Croce*. And what a fitting departure from Goa! Easter Sunday was a beautiful day to begin the journey. Surely it meant that God's blessing was on it. Everybody was full of kindness and helpfulness during those last days. Many of them even shared his own enthusiasm for the venture. The people of Goa had faith. He warmed at the recollection of the pleasant leave-taking. He knew he took with him their affection and their prayers. And now here was Malacca already. Pereira would be waiting and they would have to unload and load cargo. But the hard part was over. The mission to China was really underway.

Father Francis was ready to go ashore. He took his place in the little boat as it pushed away. He scanned the familiar waterfront eagerly. Suddenly he realized that something was strange. The waterfront seemed deserted. What was the matter with Malacca? There was none of the usual life and bustle on the praya. Nobody was there. He felt a slight sense of foreboding. As the boat touched, he saw a loitering sailor. He stepped ashore and made for him.

The man stared at him in apparent surprise. "Don't you know, Father?" he said. "We have the plague here. Half the town has it. Even the Commandant is down with it, and they say he is a very sick man. If you want to find anybody, my advice to you is to look for him in the hospital." The man paused. "Or the cemetery," he added. "Good-bye, Father," he ended, as the missioner passed on.

The plague! No wonder the town had lost its animation and did not seem itself. The scourge would prostrate the place, of course, and many a poor, unprepared soul would pass to the Judgment Seat of God before it ran its course. The instinctive chill of foreboding deepened but it lasted only a moment. He shook it off with a little laugh, as his mind went forward to his own plans. "Just means some work to do," he told himself. "Better get busy. There would be a long wait here anyhow, so it makes little difference. And the Commandant! Why, come to think of it, maybe that is providential. Not too sure of that good man, somehow. Something worldly and artificial about him. But here is his new appointment right in my pocket and that ought to please him. Captain-General-of-the-Sea is high-sounding enough, surely. Odd how these empty-headed officials like empty titles. It's good the Governor decided to give it to him. Comes just at the right time. Now if we can get him well and on his feet again, there shouldn't be any trouble."

At first the Commandant was too sick to recognize his new nurse. Father Francis stole a lot of time from his busy ministrations in the jammed hospital to take personal care of him. People were dying right and left and the missioner had to multiply himself. He worked all day and most of the night at every sort of task — bringing medicine and food, changing linen, washing clothes, listening to troubles, taking last messages, giving the Last Sacraments — and then threw himself on the corridor floor in a corner to snatch a few scanty hours of sleep. But he was in and out of the Commandant's room continually seeing to his every want, and from the time the sick man began to recover, the missioner set up the altar in his room and said Mass there for him every day.

166

Father Francis could not tell if the Commandant liked his new appointment. He took the document that made him Captain-General-of-the-Sea with a formal bow, and did not even thank the missioner for bringing it. Father Francis wondered a little. He felt chilled. But he knew no reason for displeasure. He smiled. A government official has many cares. No doubt his mind was engaged with something else.

It seemed too good to be true, but the *Santa Croce* was all fittedout and ready to clear for China. Diego Pereira had loaded his good ship with every sort of merchandise to impress the Chinese and was ready to qualify as an Ambassador to the Orient bearing gifts. Father Xavier had gathered together his little band of missioners and seen to their last-minute preparations.

It was indeed too good to be true, for then the blow fell. The word went around Malacca suddenly and with equal speed came to Father Francis. The *Santa Croce* cannot sail! The Commandant will not have any embassy to China! He took away the ship's rudder and hung it up over his office! Pereira is not Ambassador! He has no appointment! It's all a scheme of Father Xavier's and he is an impostor! Another case of a priest meddling in affairs that do not concern him! Why does Father Xavier have to go to China? May anger the Chinese Emperor and cause plenty of trouble! Why can't he stay here and mind his own business?

Father Xavier went straight to the Commandant's office. He was told that the Commandant did not want to see him. "Well, maybe not," he replied, "but I want to see him." He strode into the office.

"Did you order the *Santa Croce* not to sail? And why?"

167

He threw his question at the Commandant directly. He stood waiting for an answer.

The Commandant shifted uneasily in his chair. He put up the hand of expostulation. "Now listen, Father," he began, "and I will explain to you how it is." He shifted around again and looked at the ceiling. He fumbled with the papers on his desk. "You see, it's this way, Father," he continued. "Pereira is not Ambassador—."

"Wait a minute," interrupted the missioner. "Who said he wasn't? He was appointed by the Governor of Goa who has full authority."

"Well, I cannot let him sail. I do not judge that such an expedition is in the best interests of the Portuguese Crown. I am charged with those interests in these areas, especially since I have been appointed Captain-General-of-the-Sea. It is my responsibility."

"It's not your responsibility to countermand the appointment of your own superior officer. How are you going to explain this to the Governor of Goa? I will see that he hears about it. And the King of Portugal besides."

The Commandant was stung. He jumped up. "Get out of my office," he shouted. "I am in charge of affairs here. I won't talk with a man like you."

Father Francis smiled for the first time. He did not stir. "Won't you?" he replied. "Perhaps then you will listen. This expedition is perfectly in order. Diego Pereira is the official Ambassador appointed by the Governor. He has all his credentials. Besides, he has already invested a great sum of money in the expedition, so he will face a severe loss if he does not go. As for myself, I have the appointment as Apostolic Nuncio from the Holy Father in Rome, charging me

168

with the duty of devising means for the spread of the Faith in all these regions. This is a necessary expedition and a fully authorized one. The embassy to China may result in opening that great country to the Faith. Millions are dying there without it. This may be the means of converting the whole Far East. I cannot forego this opportunity. And do you not want to share in it? Think what it would mean to be an instrument in such a work for the Church. God would surely bless you."

"I don't care if Pereira loses his money," the febrile, twitching Commandant shouted. "He was foolish to spend it in the first place. I don't care if you are the Papal Nuncio. I don't believe it, either. I won't have anything to do with this crazy expedition. The embassy is not going. And you get out of here."

The missioner looked at the excited man sadly. He turned to depart. "God bring you to a better mind, my good Commandant," he said slowly. He strode out.

It was only the beginning. Everything went wrong. The whole settlement was agog with rumors concerning the ill-fated expedition that had been so talked about and was now ending in nothing. The gossipy community enjoyed its little tempest in a teapot to the full. Father Francis suddenly found himself a laughing-stock. Forgotten were all the labors and feats of mercy he had performed for the people of Malacca on so many occasions. Even his heroic work for the plague-stricken people in the hospital a short week ago had gone into the limbo of forgotten things. He did not know the extent of the changed atmosphere until he found acquaintances passing him by in the streets without any sign of recognition.

People walked away from him. Twice he heard catcalls

and jeers flung after him as he passed down the street. Even the children caught the contagion. "Crazy Padre! Crazy Padre!" came a shout from a group of boys as they scampered around a corner of the street. That cut him a little. He had been such friends with Malacca's children when he rounded them up to teach them catechism. He checked himself. "It's not from their hearts," he told himself. "They know no better." He was not going to be too much disturbed by the new attitude. "I had Palm Sunday in this place often enough," he reflected. "It's time I had a chance to be treated like my Lord and Master."

What really worried him was the disintegration of his mission venture. Almost overnight the rosy prospect had changed completely. The Commandant had plenty of power to stop the embassy, even if he did not have the legal authority. Nothing would move against his orders. Pereira could not go as Ambassador. Father Francis had had to deprive himself of Father Gago and send him straight to Japan for a sudden emergency. Brother Alvaro was scared and reluctant. Christopher, the Tamil boy, was flighty and undependable. He had already made trouble. Antonio was the only real prop left, and now it turned out that he had forgotten almost all his Chinese speech and would be of little practical help. The whole outlook was forbidding. His wonderful plan had suddenly dwindled to almost nothing. Yesterday the opening of a continent was within his grasp. Today he was again a lone missioner against the world.

To penetrate the forbidden land as an unwanted lawbreaker was the alternative left. It was neither a pleasant nor a promising one, but Father Francis had no intention of turning back. The kind old Vicar General of Malacca remonstrated with the Commandant, but was unable to change his attitude about the proposed embassy. There was nothing for the missioner to do but go on to Sancian Island on the *Santa Croce* as part of the usual trading expedition. He could try to find some means of stealing into China from there. Father Francis lost no time in making the arrangements. It was the worst of all ways to get to China. But it was a way and he would take it.

The Vicar General and old Pereira came down to the praya to see them off on the *Santa Croce*. Nobody else bothered. The forlorn little party gathered on the foreshore. Both Alvaro and Christopher looked downcast and spiritless. Evidently they were setting out without any enthusiasm. Only Antonio seemed cheerful as he bustled about roping up the hand-luggage. Father Francis was unsmiling. It was not the leave-taking he had expected from Malacca. He turned to look back at the ungrateful city. "God forgive you," he murmured. "I hope you have not kept the Faith of Christ out of China. We will try it this way and see." He stepped into the shallop to start for the *Santa Croce*. He squared his shoulders and faced the open sea.

DOWRY
for ANITA

EXCEPT for one soli-
tary figure, the beach appeared to be deserted. The worn-
looking man pacing the sands in his tattered black cassock was the priest who had come to Sancian Island in an
attempt to penetrate forbidden China. His hopes met with
ridicule on all sides, but he went his own way and kept his
own counsel.

Almost at any time he could be seen haunting the beach,
walking sometimes with head bent in prayer, sometimes with
eyes raised to the sky as if in some inner exultation, often
with restive glances that roved across the bay to where the
mountains of the mainland sprawled; bald and ungainly
sentinels that seemed to form an impassable barrier to the
mysterious Empire of China, closed and unknown for centuries. But to the priest they only seemed to beckon. Barrier was not in his dictionary. He was Francis Xavier.

He often chose this period of the day because he was practically certain to have the beach to himself. But today, as he
reached the end of the strand and was just turning for another stretch down its length, he was surprised to find suddenly that he was not entirely alone. Out on the point,
slumped down on the rocks and looking to sea, was a
figure even stranger to that part of the world than his own.
He looked closer.

"Strange," he ejaculated. "Unless my eyes are getting

172

queer, it's a Portuguese woman. Now what in heaven's name can a Portuguese woman be doing on this island?" He sauntered over to his unusual find. Closer inspection revealed a girl rather than a woman; the dejected young person crouched on the rocks was only in her late teens. He noted a pitiful attempt at finery in the dowdy artificial flowers of her drooping hat.

His first salutation went unanswered. After several attempts, he got a monosyllable. Finally she flung around in petulance. "What am I doing here?" She saw the cassock. "Oh, excuse me, Father," she checked herself. "Why — really I — I hardly know myself."

"It's an odd place for a young girl like you," he told her. "I suppose you came with your father. But you ought not to wander around alone."

"I didn't come here with my father. My father is in Malacca."

"Oh." The priest considered this a moment. "Surely you did not come to Sancian Island all alone?"

"No, Father. I didn't come alone. I came with — with my — husband."

"With your husband!" This time the priest was genuinely surprised. None of the merchants ever dreamed of bringing their wives to Sancian. The place was quite rough enough for men. He went to the point. "Where is your husband, my child?"

"He told me to wait here. Our matshed is down on the other beach. He went over to see Senhor Velho about something, and said he would be back in a moment. That was a half hour ago."

"He ought not to leave you sitting here like this. The

island is a wild place, and anything might happen to you."

"Father!" The girl's defenses were breaking down. She stole a look at the priest's face; saw only kindness. "Father, he is not really my husband, in a way. You see, we —" She broke off, and turned away.

"Never mind, never mind," he soothed. "Whatever the trouble is, there is always a way out of it. You mean that you are not married, don't you? Well, that is quite an omission, no doubt. But it is one that we can easily supply. Now tell me. Who is your husband, my child? And who are you?"

"My name is Anita Carvalho, Father. We live in Malacca. His is Rodrigo Henriques."

He soon had the rest of the story.

Two young people, unable to obtain parental consent, had in a foolish moment stowed away on one of the boats bound for Sancian, and thought to call it a marriage. That was two months ago, and now the girl at least was sorry. Of course, she wanted to be married. And her husband was willing to get it straightened out also. That is, provided a dowry could be supplied in some way. That was what had caused the trouble in the first place. It was all a question of the dowry.

"But the Church does not demand a dowry, child," protested Xavier finally, when he had sifted the matter down to this point.

"Maybe not, Father," she replied, "but his parents do. That's the reason they would not give their consent, and so we couldn't get married."

Xavier paused. It was a serious difficulty, as he had reason to know. He had patched up marriages of the same sort before. Not that it made any difference whether the parents consented or not; only if they held out for the dowry, the

174

son would doubtless do the same, fearing to be cut off. It was a very ingrained custom, and Xavier was too good a missioner to try to brush it impatiently aside. He mused a bit before replying.

"Well, Anita," he said finally, "it looks to me as if my very first task is to get you a dowry. I must say I doubt if it will be easy to find on this island. Still, all things are possible with God." He looked at his companion. Where all had been dejection before, he now saw a face lit with hope. He became the man of action.

"Where did you say your husband was? In Velho's matshed? Well now, that is what I call convenient. Here's where I kill two birds with one stone. Now listen. You go home and put on your best dress. How long will that take? About an hour? All right. And then come out to the little chapel on the point. You know it, don't you? Leave the rest to me, and don't you worry one little bit. I'll be at the chapel waiting for you. And I'll bring dowry, husband, best man, and everything else along with me. Even flowers, if you want. Is that a bargain? See you later."

Loud voices were coming from Pedro Velho's matshed when the tattered black cassock approached it a few minutes later. He entered to find a card game going on. Fortune favored him, which is to say, Divine Providence. The game was for high stakes, and the impecunious young husband he sought was contenting himself with looking on. "Keep on with your game," he said, after the first greetings. "Perhaps this young man and I can entertain each other." He flashed the smile that had thrilled the King of Portugal.

The young man found himself being drawn into an animated conversation, and before long he was continuing it in a stroll outside. Xavier made short work of him. After a quarter of an hour, he sent the boy back home to brighten himself up for his wedding. Xavier breathed more freely, though the hardest part was yet to come. He returned to the matshed.

Francis Xavier did not bother much about skirmishing for openings. Once he had a definite goal, he took the straightest road. Asking favors was a matter of routine. As he asked them always for God or His service, and never for himself, he saw no reason to hesitate. The man who owned the matshed was his chosen prey. Pedro Velho was a good friend. A man of much faith and little practice, as was common among the merchants, Pedro possessed stout outlines and a jolly disposition, and was a type who could be induced fairly easily to contribute to almost any good cause. He did not usually do so, however, without some show of resistance.

"I hope you are winning, Pedro," began Father Xavier, starting right in the middle of things, "because something tells me you are going to need some money."

"I generally do when you are around, Father." Pedro kept on playing cards, but suspicion was born. He knew Xavier's approach. "What's on your mind now?"

"A little matter of a dowry for our two young people. You'll never miss it. I am going to marry them in an hour."

"Dowry for young people!" Velho dropped his cards. "What young people? Am I their uncle or something? Dowry! Why drag me into it? Have a little mercy, can't you?"

"It's this way, Pedro. That young Henriques who was just here isn't really married. Neither is his wife — naturally. It's a question of the dowry. You probably know the case, although I only just now found it out."

"Well, Father Francis, suppose I do know the case? How does that elect me to pay the dowry?" Pedro was contesting with two opponents against whom he had very little chance of success. One was Father Xavier, and the other was his own generous heart. "I confess the girl is very poor. I know her people in Malacca. They haven't a cent. But what has that got to do with me?"

"You are rich, Pedro. God has been good to you. Undoubtedly it is because He wants you to lend a hand to others less fortunate."

"Rich!" protested Pedro. "Fine chance anybody has to be rich with you around! With your dowries, and one thing and another!"

"Well, it's for God, after all. It isn't much to ask for Him."

Pedro was visibly weakening. He sighed. "How much is it, Father?"

"Only a hundred ducats. You'll never miss it, Pedro."

"Never miss it! A hundred ducats! You priests certainly are a cool lot, the way you talk about money. I wish you had to earn a hundred ducats once. Why, I'll be lucky if I make that much profit on the whole trip," he grumbled. It was his last stand. He looked around for encouragement from the others. He got none. They knew he was going to be the loser in this tilt with Father Xavier. They were waiting patiently for the finish, so that they could resume the interrupted game of cards.

Pedro sighed again and gave in. He pulled out his keys. "Go and get a hundred ducats out of my strong box on the ship; will you, Father? I don't carry a sum like that around with me. They told me to look out for pirates when we left

177

Malacca. But how am I to escape the clutches of a pirate like you?"

He passed over the keys, which Xavier accepted with alacrity. "Just ask the young couple to say a prayer for an old sinner; will you, Father? And say one yourself, please. I don't know but one of yours is probably worth it." Pedro smiled sheepishly, still dissembling the patent fact that he was a cheerful giver and a good loser.

Xavier stopped and said the prayer then and there. Pedro was turning back to his cards when suddenly Father Francis bent over him earnestly. "God bless you, Pedro," he said. "It is strange, but I have an intimation that your generosity will be rewarded. Shall I tell you how?"

Pedro laughed. "Yes, please do, Father. I shall surely need a reward after you get finished making a pauper out of me."

"Here is what I am minded to tell you. You will not die amid all these dangers that surround you now. You will live to a good old age. And then there will be a sign. When the wine tastes sour in your mouth, prepare."

"Father Francis! You are fooling." Pedro looked closer to see if he was serious or not. "Well, thanks, anyhow. I must say it is a pretty consoling forecast. Believe me, when good wine tastes sour to Pedro, he'll be ready. Wouldn't want to live after that, anyhow."

And so there was a marriage on Sancian Island, performed by a saint.

Years later a jolly old merchant in Macao was enjoying his usual glass of wine, when suddenly he found the taste bitter in his mouth, and by the time he could make his soul's peace and prepare for his last journey, he had gone to join the man who wheedled him out of a dowry for the love of God.

178

EVER LESS ALONE

HE felt queer, light-headed, a little unsteady on his feet, as he began to say Mass. He thought it was because he had been cutting corners on sleep. Not that he was very busy, but he had been giving lavish hours to long bursts of rapt prayer. A mild resolve to get more sleep flashed through his mind. He lurched on his feet a little and grasped the edge of the rude altar to support himself when Antonio presented the wine and water. He felt dizzy. And what made it so hot all of a sudden? Had the weather changed? The cool, fresh wind of South China's idyllic November stole through the gaping apertures of the ramshackle little hut, even as he thought about it. The candles flickered. The breeze was refreshing, but he was still parched and hot. Then he completely forgot about it, as he extended his hands over the chalice and the little bell tinkled.

This is My Body. The white Host gleamed aloft for an instant in his trembling hands. *This is the chalice of My Blood . . . which shall be shed for you and for many unto the remission of sins.* He braced himself as he raised and lowered the chalice with infinite care. On the instant the whole universe changed. He was no longer just a fever-wracked wanderer, stranded at the end of the world with little hope of going on and still less of return. "Why, You came with me. You are here — and I want nothing," was the instinctive thought that flashed across his mind. He was where he belonged — and the whole heavenly court was with him. It was not a new thought. It was one that had come to him countless times since that day many years ago when he first stood at the altar to welcome the Living Bread that came down from heaven. It had been more and more with him in the recent years of his long, lonely voyages. He dismissed it now with a conscious effort and went on slowly and painstakingly with the Mass. But his soul felt lifted as if on wings.

He was a little embarrassed to be caught huddled up on the floor when Antonio returned with three of the Portuguese sailors from the *Santa Croce*. But he really was feeling very ill. He had known the Chinese boy was up to something when he left the hut that afternoon. The missioner's refusal to eat all day had plainly worried his faithful young companion. He did not think he would feel any better on the ship, but it was kind of these good men to come for him. He knew that from the Captain down they already thought he was a little crazy to have remained on the island, and he did not wish to estrange them further. He decided to let them take him along.

The Captain met him. "I told you that Chinese boat would never come back for you, Father Francis," was his greeting. "Not a chance in my opinion. They have your bargain money, and that's all they wanted."

The sick man did not find this very consoling. But he was too sick to feel that it mattered much. He rallied his forces to return a kindly answer. "It is good of you to take me aboard, Captain," he replied. "I am not feeling very well. I should like to wait a little longer for the boat to China. It is only a few days overdue. Any little accident could have delayed it. It will be as God wills."

180

The sound of retching and stifled groans stopped a sailor leaving his watch the next morning and brought him into the missioner's tiny cabin. The wind had freshened during the night, and the ship was dancing and rolling. One glance showed that the prostrate sick man was finding it very trying. His labored breath, flushed face and restless limbs made him a picture of misery. Antonio was watching beside him, looking his own misery. The sailor went to call the medical officer and the Captain.

"We'll take the Father back," said the Captain, after he and the doctor had seen the sick priest and listened to Antonio. "The doctor will go with him and bleed him for the fever. The ship is rolling too much." He bent over the sick man. His look was kindly, as if he meant to comfort him. "I'll call a sampan and put you back on shore, Father Francis," he said. "Maybe the fresh air will help you. But I told you you should have gone back with our fleet when it started for Malacca day before yesterday. No use staying in this desolate place. But anyhow, we'll do what we can for you."

The priest thanked him. With the help of Antonio and one of the sailors he staggered out of the cabin. He almost fell into the water as they guided him into the little sampan. The Captain wrapped a coarse ship's blanket around his shoulders. The sailor reached in his pocket and gave Antonio a handful of almonds as the sampan was pushing off. The man burning with fever did not need either, but he looked his gratitude for the simple acts.

Antonio got more and more worried as the days passed. The bleeding had had no effect except to make the sick man weaker. Visitors to the little hut were few. Except for the simple fishermen of the island, Sancian was deserted. All the traders had left. The market place was dismantled. Christopher, the Tamil boy, looked in once, but Father Francis had not seemed pleased with him. He roused himself from his torpor to scold the boy about his bad conduct, but Christopher only looked sullen and hung his head and said nothing. The boy slunk away and did not come back again. After that nobody came and Antonio remained with the priest alone.

Mostly the sick man lay in a stupor, but at times when the fever was strong, he seemed to pass into a state of delirium. Then he spoke rapidly, sometimes raising his voice to a shout and again trailing off in a whisper. Antonio did not understand the languages he was speaking. Most of his talk sounded like the Latin of the psalms he had heard in the churches at Goa and Malacca. There was another language that sounded very much like Portuguese and yet was not Portuguese, and there was another that rang out more sonorous than either. There were snatches of the catechism in Tamil and in Japanese. And there was one language completely strange — and this he seemed to speak more flowingly and meaningfully than any other, as if it might have been the language of his inmost thoughts from his childhood. Antonio could only sit and wonder. He could not get the missioner to eat anything. He watched him growing weaker day by day.

Father Francis wanted the crucifix. It helped him to pray. He took it from the boy, kissed it, and propped it on the blanket where he could see it without turning his head. "Everything went wrong," he whispered. "But if it is right with You, it is right with me." The effort was difficult for him. He did not try to speak again.

182

His mind was clear, and he let his thoughts wander. China just across the bay. He would never reach it. That trouble with the Commandant at Malacca was fatal. God forgive the poor man. If only we could have gone with our own Ambassador! That was the way to get to China. Might still go with the Ambassador of Siam? But when is he going — and will he take me? Nobody knows. Maybe I should have gone back with the ships to Malacca. Was I just foolish — and stubborn? This wasn't the best way to get to China. Brother Alvaro deserted me. Christopher is lost to me. Anthony has forgotten all his Chinese. The boat hasn't come. And here I am. Everything went wrong from the start. But I couldn't go back — I had to keep on. Ignatius will understand. And so will You. He felt comforted. He smiled. He had made his report. The crucifix slid off the blanket. His eyes were closed and he did not notice it. He seemed asleep.

Antonio watched him closely. His head lay listless on the sacking that took the place of a pillow. His breathing was faint. Antonio thought it was time. He picked up the crucifix and propped it up on the matting where the missioner could see it when he opened his eyes. The boy saw his lips moving as if in prayer, but no sound came forth. He arose and got the little stub of Mass candle that was left. He lighted it and held it against the missioner's nerveless hand, as he had seen the priests do in Malacca.

The lips were still moving. It must be a long prayer. There was the trace of a smile, as if the haggard face were lit up by some inner vision. Suddenly the eyes opened. They reached towards the crucifix. The sick man strained forward. He had come to the end of his prayer. "*In Te, Domine, speravi non confundar in æternum,*" came the Latin words halt-

183

ingly but in a clear, strong voice. The missioner sank back on the tumbled matting. Antonio heard a little sigh, almost as if a breath of wind had stirred through the hut. There was the slightest of tremors and the gaunt form lay inert. Antonio leaned over. There was no breathing. Father Francis was still.

The candle still flickered where Antonio had set it down in the drafty hut. It was a symbol. The greatest mission undertaking in history was over. The great soul of Xavier had flown to God. But a flame had been lighted in the East that would never die.